LET'S TAKE IT FROM

ABOUT THE AUTHOR

David Bathurst has been singing in church choirs since he was eleven years old and all his adult life; he belonged to his village church choir in Surrey for seventeen years and to the choir of Boxgrove Priory in Sussex for just over twelve years. He has been a member of numerous other choirs and choral groups. His singing experience inspired him to write this book. All the events described in it, although they are fictional, are based on things which have happened to him or people he has met in the course of choir membership.

By profession David is a solicitor and legal adviser to a bench of magistrates covering the Chichester and Worthing areas of Sussex. He is married to Susan, and they have a daughter, Jennifer Rose. David has lived in the Chichester area for fifteen years, and in his spare time when not singing or looking after his family enjoys writing, cycling and walking. His most notable achievements to date have been reciting the four Gospels from memory on a single day in July 1998, and reciting the Book of Psalms, the longest book of the Bible, from memory on a single day in September 2002.

BY THE SAME AUTHOR

The Selsey Tram
Six Of The Best!
The Jennings Companion
Financial Penalties – Collection And Enforcement In Magistrates' Courts
Around Chichester In Old Photographs
Here's A Pretty Mess!
Magisterial Lore
The Beaten Track
Poetic Justice
Walking The Coastline Of Sussex
Best Sussex Walks

LET'S TAKE IT FROM THE TOP

By DAVID BATHURST

Illustrated by TERENCE WHITLOCK

with best wishes

Romansmead Publications

First published in 2003 by

Romansmead Publications
The Green House
3 Nursery Cottages
Barnham Lane
Barnham
West Sussex PO22 0JJ

Printed in England by Polestar Wheatons Limited, Hennock Road, Marsh
Barton, Exeter, Devon EX2 8RP

British Library Cataloguing-in-Publication Data.
A catalogue record for this book is available from the British Library.

ISBN 0-9523936-8-9

PROLOGUE

Dear Jackie,

A week ago tonight I was sitting in St Basil's Church for midnight mass and was aware God had spoken to me. Not through the powerful and wise words of our well-loved vicar; nor through the wondrous mystery of the Incarnation as depicted by the magnificent crib that has graced the south chapel of St Basil's every Christmas for the last hundred years; nor through the ethereal beauties of the crisp starlit night, each star an awesome revelation of God's divine power. It was the cacophonous din that was supposed to pass for the unaccompanied second verse of *Away In A Manger*. How Frank Tripplehorn, the choirmaster, thought he could get away with it when two sopranos were down with flu and the only alto had retired to the vestry after setting fire to her cassock during the candle-lit second verse of *Once In Royal*, I really cannot begin to guess. But that is the beauty of religious experience: it comes through the least probable sources. Amidst the discordant racket I sensed the voice of God, telling me that the choir needed me.

A year or even six months ago, I would have resisted any pressure to join the ranks of the St Basil's musicians. But, of course, a lot has changed since then. Principally, your leaving me for New Zealand. As suggested by that very able Relate counsellor, and the agony columnist of the magazine I read while waiting to have that wisdom tooth removed, I've tried to be positive about our newly separated state and looked for ways of getting more involved in the life of the local community. And as I'm blessed with a reasonable singing voice, the events of midnight mass have now given me that final push into full choir membership. I was asked to attend an audition on Sunday and went along with a choice of tenor arias from Handel's *Messiah*, Bach's *St John Passion* and Orff's *Carmina Burana*, unsure exactly what would be expected of me. It was an anticlimax to be accepted having sung the first line of the National Anthem in tune.

Of course, you'll remember the services you attended with me at St Basil's and the sort of church it is. In a guidebook to the area I read recently, it is described as "a 16th century jewel in an otherwise unremarkable but pleasant and bustling provincial town in the heart of Southern England." Congregations have certainly improved radically since the arrival of the new vicar although it would be nice to see a greater proportion of younger people in the pews each Sunday. I have no intention of moving from my nice home in the town, especially with the church being just walking distance away. We practise every Friday night, and to be honest it's nice to have something to occupy what would be one of the loneliest nights of the week. And since I still have my job in town, with reasonably sociable hours, there are no worries about getting to rehearsals on time. I like to think that having only just reached my fortieth birthday I am able to offer to the choir a comparatively youthful voice, combined with a fair amount of previous experience and voice training; while my stint in the Wolverhampton Polytechnic glee club is not the most impressive musical qualification it does at least give me the advantage of knowing whether I am vaguely in tune with the rest of the choir. And how many of even the top performers of today can boast of having sung an *a cappella* version of *The Laughing Policeman* at the Wolverhampton Town Hall, as I did with the glee club, dressed only in straw boaters and striped all-in-one bathing suits.

Although I have never sung with the choir before, except for one wedding, I have met a few of them through regular attendance at St Basil's, and have been filled in on the rest by Ken Foulkes, one of the basses. Frank Tripplehorn, the choirmaster, is a mercurial character who is devoted to his choir and is constantly striving to improve its standards and heighten its profile in the wider community as well as in the church. Although he has always been perfectly civil and friendly towards me, he has a reputation for stubbornness and for being almost brutally candid when he needs to be, causing a major upset as recently as two months ago when he "advised" Miranda Cobbledick that her talents no longer lay in the musical field. Rumour has it that at the same time he was hoping to oust second soprano Cora Willoughby-Smith, whose blend with the rest of the choir reminds me of the result of my recently and quite inadvertently adding two spoonfuls of Bisto powder into a weak cup of instant coffee. I honestly think he will find it easier to climb Mount Everest on a pogo stick clad only in a G-string and a pair of frogmen's flippers. Despite her apparently conceding in a rare moment of weakness that she could no longer hit the high notes required of first sopranos, she is remarkably adept at keeping for herself all the soprano solos; her skills extend to being in the centre of every choir photograph, and seeing to it that those singers who either challenge or actively resent her dominance are subtly eased out of the choir as quickly as possible, while always ensuring her own indispensability by making her house available for every big choir social event. The formidable Hazel Ledworthy and geriatric

Queenie Haverthwaite make up the rest of the second soprano section. The first sopranos are somewhat younger; Alison Sparkes usually comes with her daughter Zoe and son Matthew, and slightly less regular but rather more proficient are Rachel Ellis, whose husband Brian sings bass, and Margaret Pardew. Poor Margaret seems doomed to eternal spinsterhood, unless the fates contrive either to kill off her elderly mother for whom she has become virtually a full-time carer, or fire her with the impetus to visit one of the boutiques in town and treat herself to a set of clothes that belong in the 21st century and not the 1950's. The altos cover every age range: Jane Markwick, a budding music student in her late teens who sadly will leave us for university in the autumn; her mother Lesley, who worships the organ stool Mr Tripplehorn sits on; Joan Trumpington, choir secretary/librarian with a reputation for chronic absent-mindedness; and Eileen Crosby, well into her seventies and sensible enough to appreciate that her days on top soprano were left behind with the days when English footballers played regularly in the Chelsea first team.

My two fellow tenors will be Craig Dumbleton, a delightful man with a passable and crucially blendable voice and an abnormally unhealthy interest in trivia in general and British Rail in the 1970's in particular, and Arthur Ramsbottom, the self-appointed choir archivist and cameraman who also happens to be the longest-serving choir member, but whose contribution to sensitive chorus tenor singing is comparable to Cyril Smith's contribution to the Southern Counties Weight Watchers Federation. Tripplehorn assures me he is next on the hit list, but I'll believe that when I see it. As for the basses, Ken Foulkes, a sprightly sixty-eight, is a stalwart choir member and has a fine rich voice; I often think he'd be happier bursting into *Old Man River* rather than intoning the gospel acclamation when the celebrant forgets to do it. Brian Ellis has a useful voice and is sensible enough to sing the tune an octave lower if he gets lost rather than bring his own experimental harmonies into the arena. Then there's Henry Peasgood, who although his better singing days are behind him, can always go musically one better than you; if you've sung Beethoven's Ninth on Sydney Harbour Bridge, he will have sung Britten's *War Requiem* on a tightrope above the Niagara Falls. Lastly is the rather morose and laconic Irving Cattermole, who often has to dash off after communion to play the organ for mattins at St Bartholomews in the neighbouring village of the same name, the congregation of which, he keeps telling everyone, consists of "two men and a dog." When I saw him at midnight mass I remarked that either they breed very religious canines in St Bartholomews or Mrs Spinks, the crusty churchwarden of St Basil's, has

7

started attending there as well. It was unfortunate that she turns out to be his sister.

So what has prompted me to want to chronicle a year of my membership of St Basil's? Well, you yourself said you were anxious for me to keep in touch with you and keep you up to speed on things at home. But also it's a good opportunity to offer an insight into the realities of church choir life and the demands of serving God in an increasingly secular society with its own problems and pressures. The parish church choir is something of an institution in the Church of England, but nothing is certain; should there come a time, God forbid, when traditional church music-making ceases to exist, I would like to think this diary would provide a kind of memento of the days when churches on Sunday mornings did echo to the sounds of Stanford, Stainer and Vaughan Williams. Or at least to an approximation of the sounds these composers intended. I'm also interested to see whether this record of a year of serving the Lord through choir membership will confirm or dispel the theory that those whom God is not calling to preach to primitive cannibalistic tribes in the remote jungles of South America are necessarily having a much easier time in doing his earthly work. From what I can gather, even the sound of natives executing a blood-curdling wardance of delight round the missionary's cooking pot must rank as positively celestial compared with the warbling of Cora Willoughby-Smith in her quest for the wings of a dove.

JANUARY

Tuesday 1st January

My debut with the choir of St Basil's, consisting of a 12 noon service to commit the New Year to the Lord. It was a very frosty, icy morning and it was no surprise to see only a few cars scattered about the church car park. I arrived at just the same time as Hazel Ledworthy, and we proceeded up the path together. As we walked, a man a short way in front of us slipped and fell spectacularly to the ground. I turned to Hazel Ledworthy and joked "He obviously had a good night last night." "I shouldn't think so," she replied brusquely. "His leg's not been right since his stroke two years ago. He's probably quite seriously hurt." And with that she hurried up to the prostrate body and started making arrangements with his companions for an ambulance.

Not the most auspicious first step in my quest to gain acceptance in the ranks.

As soon as I arrived in the vestry, I made a beeline for Joan Trumpington and asked if she had organised a robe for me. It was clear from the look on her face that she had not given it a moment's thought despite the three occasions I had mentioned it over the preceding couple of days. She rummaged in the robe cupboard and produced a very long, faded garment with frayed collars and sleeves. "That used to be Mr Murgatroyd's," she said. "He did get very attached to it." Looking at the size of it, I found that hard to believe. I glanced at the label on the inside of the collar and saw that it bore the initials B.O. Unfortunately they could hardly have been more apposite. One whiff under the arms confirmed the worst. I jovially asked Irving Cattermole what happened to the robe which stank the place out with that awful 1980's Tesco after-shave, and with which I'd been saddled when I'd sung at that wedding with the choir in August. "Oh, that's mine," he said. "I've had it since 1970."

In the circumstances decided it was best not to ask him to help me do up the top left button which to attempt myself would have required the skills of a psychotic contortionist. Eventually I enlisted the services of Brian Ellis who duly obliged, but the resultant fastening sent me into such a strangulated state that I could hardly look down at the music I was supposed to be singing from. It was as well that the service was fairly undemanding – two hymns and a simple sung Amen – and as we recessed I was heaving an inward sigh of relief that I had survived thus far without garrotting myself. Until, on arrival at the chancel step which I completely forgot was there, I got my legs caught up in the bottom of the robe and crashed down on to the floor of the nave. The vicar's first words to me once I had made it back to the vestry were "You obviously had a good night last night." I really couldn't be bothered to reply.

Wednesday 2nd January

Joan Trumpington popped my "choir welcome brochure" through my letter box this evening, promising that tomorrow I should receive details of the choir events for the year, and on Sunday I will have a new robe. I see that my choir number is 48. Since it is believed that the last time there were 48+ choir members was either for a special service to celebrate the Coronation of Elizabeth II, or the time it was rumoured Pamela Anderson was attending a wedding in the church in the capacity of topless bridesmaid, I am still not sure of the logic behind this. I suppose it's an improvement on my experience with Vox Dicentis, a choral group I belonged to for a single term a couple of years back, when every piece of music or choir documentation I was given was marked "SPARE." I'm sure they were trying to tell me something. Then again, to judge by the way Hazel Ledworthy regarded me during yesterday morning's service I suppose I ought to be grateful I've not been given the number 666.

Thursday 3rd January

The timetable of choir events arrived today. Some of them do look quite fun, I have to say. I'm looking forward to Stainer's *Crucifixion* on Palm Sunday, the choir concert in May ("sensible ideas please"), the choir summer party in late July ("don your chef's hats"), the choir outing to Lyme Regis in October ("husbands, wives, sisters, cousins and aunts welcome, coach leaves 9am sharp") and recording our very own CD during the autumn ("our own tilt at stardom!"). Rather less ecstatic about the early start on Easter Sunday morning for the sunrise vigil on Castle Hill ("in the church if wet"). And positively unenthusiastic about the choir's contribution to a "Come And Praise Convention" in London during March ("get your tambourines out, let your inhibitions fly"). When I last attended a similar-sounding event as a choir member – it may well have been as the Vox Dicentis spare part – my abiding memories were queuing for a quarter of an hour for the privilege of purchasing a bread roll with three inches of rubber inside, waiting even longer than that to use the latrine in the corner of the bottom field, and repeating the words "You Are Lord, We Are Yours" to the same six chords a total of 56 times.

Friday 4th January

My first choir practice tonight. I arrived slightly early and because nobody else was there, save Tripplehorn who was busy sorting out music in the vestry, I passed the time by flicking through one or two books on the little bookstall at the back of the church. There was a new one there tonight called *No Half Measures With Jesus* by the Rev Aaron P. Yardhandler II and Dr Curtis Zeugfeld Junior, respectively leader of the Inner Boston People's Church For Christ, and principal of the South West Michigan Bible Academy. The essence of it is that either we throw ourselves completely into Christian commitment and service, or we don't bother at all, and surrender ourselves to the powers of darkness.

The rehearsal finished slightly ahead of its scheduled 9pm finishing time in order that we could discuss one or two administrative matters. It had been agreed before Christmas that as from mid-January we would have coffee or tea at the end of each practice, and at this first rehearsal of the New Year, every choir member would pay a few pounds to finance the cost of the refreshment. Stung into action by the flowery transatlantic prose of Messrs Yardhandler and Zeugfeld, I found myself volunteering to bank the money and buy the provisions. I may even find time tomorrow to open a building society account for the purpose. In discipleship stakes it may not rank up there with proclaiming the message of eternal salvation in Christ to Communist secret police, drug-crazed dropouts on the streets of Rio de Janeiro, or late night Channel 5 audiences, but it's a start.

As I was leaving, Tripplehorn asked if I'd lead the choir in for the Epiphany procession on Sunday morning. Apparently that honour has traditionally fallen to Arthur Ramsbottom, but, he went on cryptically, "after what happened last year, it's better someone with a brain actually does it." I do vaguely remember something going awry last year. I think either he dropped his music on to Avril Blenkinsop's foot, or led the whole choir into the broom cupboard instead of the vestry. I know I'm quite capable of either.

Saturday 5th January

Into town this morning to open the choir's coffee and biscuit account, armed with an envelope containing an assortment of notes and coins. I decided to use the West Shires Building Society – whose current slogan is "We serve so that you save" according to the advertising jingle I heard no less than 14 times on my car radio yesterday afternoon – and arrived to find a queue of wartime proportions for the privilege of being served by one of just two overworked counter clerks, with the other five windows all shut. When eventually, after what seemed an eternity, I did reach the head of the queue, and announced I wished to open an account, I was told that I would need to see one of the Customer Service Advisers. "Surely that's not necessary," I said. "It's only a bog standard account I want."

"I'm sorry, sir," the cashier replied, "I'm not authorised. Dawn should be able to see you in a few minutes."

That prophecy proved to be rather too optimistic, as half an hour later I was still waiting. At long last, the aforesaid Dawn appeared, and without any prompting from me she launched herself into the merits of the Treasurers Plus Account, the Bronze Bonus Account, the Investor First Account, and the Cash Easy Account. Or was it the Cash First Account? After much head scratching we settled on the Treasurers Plus Account, but not before Dawn had attempted to talk me into entrusting all my other worldly goods to the West Shires Building Society, possibly through their Action First Account, the Professional Alliance Account, the Diamond Double Account, or the Platinum Retrieval Account. My having spurned these tempting propositions, there followed a further lengthy delay while the identification I had brought was checked as sufficient, a seven page form was completed, requiring me to state everything from my mother's maiden name to my dentist's inside leg measurement, a passbook was completed, and my money counted – it not helping that the contents of the envelope came to £5.02p short of the minimum sum required to open the account and I only had another fiver on me. Dawn then left me for what was another twenty-five minutes, returning to say that she was very sorry but the computer at South Shields had crashed and consequently it wouldn't be possible to process the new account today and could I come back on Monday.

I'm now thinking of writing a book entitled *What They Don't Teach You At The South West Michigan Bible Academy.*

Sunday 6th January – *EPIPHANY*

My first Sunday in the choir of St Basil's, and it was nice to see a good full church for Epiphany Sunday. I duly got my new robe, although I was marginally perplexed to see traces of what looked like lipstick on the surplice. The cassock was a bit grubby as well. I think it's a coffee stain. The anthem was Tripplehorn's own arrangement of *We Three Kings Of Orient Are.* As we lined up before the service, I whispered to Henry Peasgood that as a child I'd always wondered where the kingdoms of Aury and Tar were located. He appeared not to understand what I was going on about. He also insisted on singing "Brightest and best *are* the sons of the morning" in the first verse of the hymn of that name, rather than "*of* the sons of the morning" which irritated me so much that when we came to the last verse, with exactly the same words as the first, I thought I would sing the correct version twice as loudly. Unfortunately I totally forgot that the words of the last verse being identical to those of the first, we were omitting it, and consequently I found myself singing the words on my own. And, to add insult to injury, I sang "*are* the sons of the morning" as well.

I had to lead the procession back to the vestry at the end of the service. Was making my way confidently up the home straight, attired in a decent-fitting decent-smelling robe, and grateful that I had at least got that right, when I noticed one or two embarrassed looks on the faces of the congregation. I looked back to find that I was again on my own, the rest of the choir having stopped by the crib for a final blessing some twenty yards back and just left me to continue. Sheepishly I made my way back to the group, unable to avoid noticing a broad smirk on Matthew Sparkes' face.

Once we were all back in the vestry, I couldn't resist pointing out that Tripplehorn had said nothing about the stop at the crib. "He did, actually," said Henry Peasgood, "but some of us were still in the kingdoms of Aury and Tar."

Yet I'm swore I heard him, as we left, muttering "One in a taxi, two in a car."

Monday 7th January

Back to the West Shires Building Society. Waited in an even longer queue than on Saturday only to be told that Dawn had now been transferred to a branch 35 miles away and that there was no record of my application on their books at all. I pointed out that the only reason Dawn couldn't finalise my application was because the computer had crashed. "In that case," the cashier snapped, "it's not surprising there's no record, is it?"

Staggered out of their offices half an hour later having at last completed the paperwork and procured the passbook, and returned to my desk. I casually glanced at the passbook and saw the account had been opened in the name of CHRIO OG ST BALSA.

Bang goes my lunch-hour tomorrow.

Thursday 10th January

The post brought an appeal for all members of St Basil's to think about ways of making money to save the rapidly crumbling church roof.

Having sung through the entire *Carols For Choirs* volume 1 with the Wolverhampton Polytechnic Glee Club, and raised £250 to pay for the local homeless people to have a meal on Christmas Day, I rang Mr Swinderby, the secretary of the Finance and General Purposes Committee of the PCC, and

said I'd try and persuade some of my fellow choir members to do something similar. He thought it was a splendid idea and suggested I liaised with Tripplehorn. I decided to get on to the choirmaster straight away, hoping that having stitched me up with that Epiphany procession fiasco, he would feel he owed me one at least. When I rang him, however, he merely responded "Wouldn't it just be easier to do what my brother did on Children In Need day and sit in a bath of cold porridge for four hours?"

Absolutely. Providing I could be the one to throw him in.

Friday 11th January

Excitement at choir tonight as Tripplehorn produced copies of *With Angel Voices*, described as a compendium of church anthems old and new. He expressed particular delight that one of the pieces was *Every Night Wash I My Bed*, an arrangement of a portion of Psalm 6 by his old music lecturer, the late Herbert Bumfrey, and it was this that had been crucial in persuading him to invest in the volume in the first place. Lesley Markwick insisted on giving the pages a good sniff. "I always do it with new music books," she informed Rachel Ellis. Before long the whole line of altos and a couple of the men were inhaling the aroma of freshly unpacked copy – all, that is, except Jane Markwick who was looking meaningfully at her watch. She was apparently going straight on to a party afterwards, and was dressed to kill in short skirt and stiletto heels which looked about six inches high. Indeed when Tripplehorn bade us stand up and sing a couple of scales, I thought she was going to fall over backwards into Craig Dumbleton's arms. What with the intoxicating smell of the newly unwrapped pages, I doubt if the man had had as much excitement in one evening since being allowed into the driver's cab of the London Bridge to Catford stopping service at the age of twelve and a half.

The book is divided into three sections: Section 1 consisting of anthems "which can be attempted by any choir on minimum rehearsal and with minimum resources involving unison singing or basic harmonies;" Section 2 consisting of "more difficult pieces with more intricate harmonies," and Section 3 consisting of "demanding pieces requiring a high standard of musicianship." Tripplehorn chose to start us on one of the pieces in Section 2, not the Psalm 6 setting but a piece with an Epiphany flavour to be performed on Sunday week. The sopranos got badly bogged down on the third page resulting in some serious note-bashing, the monotony only relieved for me by reading the splendidly patronising anti-photocopying warnings at the bottom of each page, from BY PHOTOCOPYING YOU ARE DEPRIVING MUSIC PUBLISHERS OF THEIR BREAD AND

BUTTER on page twenty-six to PHOTOCOPYING IS THEFT – WE WILL PRESS FOR PROSECUTION IN EVERY CASE on page fifty-eight. Perhaps fortunately we moved on to something else so I was left to speculate as to what was promised for those wicked transgressors on subsequent pages. A devastating expose on *Crimewatch*, perhaps. Or, for the very worst offenders, an invitation to Cora Willoughby-Smith's *Ring Cycle* Singalong.

Saturday 12th January

The morning post brought a letter from West Shires Building Society welcoming me into their loving arms, offering assistance on every aspect of my business and personal financial affairs, and advising me that the choir account has been opened in the sum of minus one hundred and fifty pounds. And, for reasons best known to themselves, their "instant action helpline" is idle at weekends.

I bumped into Tripplehorn in the town's bookshop during the afternoon. Foolishly, I told him how pleased he must be to see the work of his former tutor in print. The upshot was an invitation to tea, ostensibly to make me feel welcomed and accepted in the choir, but in reality I suspect he just wanted a captive audience before whom he could lavish further praise on the man he describes as "the most under-rated church composer of the twentieth century." Apparently he has written 16 sets of responses for morning and evening prayer, 7 Passion settings, 38 mass settings, 64 psalm chants, 19 cantatas, an oratorio based on the Book of Revelation entitled *The Number Of The Beast*, and an unbelievable 127 anthems. Yet Tripplehorn seemed strangely evasive when I asked him how much of it had actually ever been published and distributed outside Bumfrey's immediate fraternity. My doubts about his popularity as a composer increased when Tripplehorn played me an extract from a rare recording of the thirtieth movement of *The Number Of The Beast*, a duet for two sopranos. The effect on my eardrums was not dissimilar to that I would expect if I were to process a pair of feral cats through an industrial shredder.

More out of politeness than anything else, I said "Perhaps we ought to have a Herbert Bumfrey Workshop Day for the choir." To my horror, Tripplehorn replied "Brilliant idea. We'll do it. We might even be able to use it to raise a bit of money for the church roof."

I'd sooner stick to the cold porridge. In every sense.

Sunday 13th January – *FIRST SUNDAY AFTER EPIPHANY – THE BAPTISM OF THE LORD*

A rather longer service than usual this morning, because of the inclusion of renewal of baptismal promises which meant our processing to the font and the consequent inclusion of an extra hymn. At least it wasn't by Herbert Bumfrey.

For the procession we sang the Epiphany hymn *Songs Of Thankfulness And Praise* which contained several mentions of the word "manifest." Zoe Sparkes happened to notice this as we were lining up before the start of the service and interrupted a conversation between her mother and Lesley Markwick to demand of her mother what the word meant. She hurriedly replied "It's what politicians publish just before an election to say what they'll do if they get into power." I somehow think the vicar's got his work cut out at Zoe's forthcoming confirmation classes.

Monday 14th January

Decided it would be much quicker just to go to the building society in person to sort out the latest problem, rather than place my faith in the telephone helpline. The cashier explained that what must have happened was that the initial fifty pounds I'd paid in had been treated as a debit entry, and when the fault was identified the computer operator tried to put it right by crediting the account with a hundred pounds but succeeded in debiting it by a further hundred pounds instead. Because the passbook entry had been made out manually, there had been no means of my identifying the error until the initial statement came through. I asked the cashier if he could rectify the problem but he advised me it wasn't as simple as that and he would be retaining my documentation while further enquiries were made. So no chance of buying the coffee, tea and bikkies required for Friday.

I don't know which prospect alarms me more: the thought that I may find myself under arrest for forgery of a West Shires passbook or sitting through a rehearsal with nothing more to look forward to by way of refreshment at the end of it than the dregs at the bottom of Hazel Ledworthy's thermos flask and whatever remains of Queenie Haverthwaite's Fisherman's Friends.

Tuesday 15th January

I got a call from Tripplehorn at work today asking if I was free this evening to help clear out some of the cupboards in the vestry, which are full of discarded sheet music. I went round after supper to find Ken Foulkes, Arthur Ramsbottom, Joan Trumpington and the choirmaster hard at work. Apparently most of the music was left there by Tripplehorn's predecessor.

When I asked Tripplehorn if some of it might not be worth airing, if only just for fun, he replied "I'd sooner have my left nipple impaled in a strand of rusty barbed wire." I do agree with him that, on the face of it, it's much more professional to sing from clean copies of nicely bound books, instead of, as he put it, "messing around with endless bits of paper that leave the choir desks looking like the summit of K9 in a snowstorm." I always thought K9 was a dog, but never mind. I do have to say, though, that I've always quite liked singing from old sheets, for a number of reasons. The sense of being in touch with our choir ancestors by singing from the same music that they once did. That somehow rather reassuring aroma of yellowing faded paper that has sat in a musty cabinet for too long. And, on the back pages, the splendid list of intriguingly titled other works by the same publisher "for the delectation of mixed voice choirs" from the sacred *They Made A Calf In Horeb* and *Over Edom Will I Cast Out My Shoe* to the secular *My Love Is A Fruit Filled Posy* and *Phyllis Played Upon Ambrosia's Fiddle*.

We discovered, buried amongst the dross, a wonderful old black and white choir photo, taken, the caption informed us, on the "annual choir outing to Bognor Pier." We all agreed the picture was none too flattering. "I wonder who that spotty little brat picking his nose in the front row is," I remarked. "He looks just the sort you'd like to give a good slap to." Arthur Ramsbottom peered at it and coldly replied "That was me." Whoops.

Thursday 17th January

As I made my way to work this morning I happened to see a big sign in Laundeasy dry-cleaners promising that for every item dry-cleaned they will dry-clean another, lower-priced, item absolutely free. Moreover, they're dry-cleaning suits at a reduced price of eight pounds fifty instead of the usual fifteen. It struck me as an excellent opportunity to get my surplice and cassock done. Anything, I thought, to gain a few extra brownie points among the membership, especially after my latest *faux pas* on Tuesday night. Today was the last day the offer applied so I hurried home and fetched my suit, and managed to persuade a churchwarden to let me into St Basil's to collect my choir vestments. I arrived back at the dry-cleaners just in time to take advantage of the same-day service.

At lunchtime I bumped into Jane Markwick, who looked just as stunning as she had last Friday. I asked her if she'd enjoyed the party and she told me that it had gone as well as could be expected, considering she and her boyfriend had split up two hours after she'd left the church . "So I'm young, free and single again," she laughed. On a whim, I asked her if she'd have a drink with me after choir tomorrow and she readily agreed. I certainly hadn't expected a potential choir romance so early in my membership, although it was a sobering thought that the last time I fixed a date with a girl singing in the same choir as me, Jane hadn't even been born.

I returned to Laundeasy just as they were shutting. Expecting to be charged simply the £8.50 for the discounted cost of the suit, I was astonished to be charged £15.

"It's the two lower-priced items that are cleaned free of charge," the gormless assistant replied.

I pointed out that individually the suit jacket and trousers came to £7.50 each and the robes were £6.95 each, and I should therefore be charged for the suit and then claim the discount.

"You can't have it both ways," the assistant told me. "You've had the robes done free, haven't you? What are you complaining about?" We ended up having a lengthy and fruitless argument and in the end I had to admit defeat. By then, however, I had wasted so much time that I was late getting home and missed the final part of an excellent early-evening drama I'd been looking forward to all day.

I'd just about composed myself when Queenie Haverthwaite rang to check I didn't need my robe for any reason next week because she was taking them all to be dry-cleaned next Monday at a specialist cleaner 20 miles away at the church's expense. Which is probably just as well, because I find that not only has the lipstick failed to come out of my surplice, but it has now run halfway down the front of it. I didn't dare check to see what effect Laundeasy's processes had done to the coffee stain on my cassock.

Friday 18th January

Despite my happy anticipation of my drink with Jane after tonight's practice, I was extremely weary throughout the rehearsal, and indeed as we set off towards the Holly Tree after coffee, Rachel Ellis commented in Jane's hearing how tired I looked. "Nonsense," I said. "I'm really looking forward to a couple of pints." As we approached the pub, Jane's mum caught us up and reminded Jane that they were going away for the weekend and she ought to be having an early night. Instead of arguing, Jane merely shrugged and disappeared down the road with her mother. Was about to leave myself when Brian, walking behind me with Rachel, said "I'll buy you a pint." Having said how much I was looking forward to the drink, I had no choice but to accept. I would in fact have been quite happy to sit with just the two of them – they're a nice couple – but as we were sitting down, Craig Dumbleton joined us and within ten minutes we found ourselves in earnest discussion about the diesel multiple units on the Charing Cross to Hastings line, with which he became very familiar as a result of visits to his elderly mother in St Leonards on Sea. Then again, I suppose every cloud has a silver lining. I may have missed out on an intimate conversation over a glass of chilled white wine with the lovely Jane Markwick, romance hanging tantalisingly in the air. But at least I now consider myself a world expert on the quality of the individual apricot pies on sale in the buffet bar at Petts Wood.

Sunday 20th January – SECOND SUNDAY AFTER EPIPHANY – WEEK OF PRAYER FOR CHRISTIAN UNITY

A service with a difference this morning, including a sermon from the local Methodist minister, prayers by the elder of the town's Baptist Church, and readings from the town's Christian Youth Fellowship attached to the evangelical church. Tripplehorn told me he hoped that any outside musical contribution would come from the Quakers. "But their worship is essentially silent, contemplative and non-musical," I pointed out. "Exactly," he said, and went off to play the pre-service voluntary.

The service started with prayers for a new resolve to demonstrate respect, tolerance and understanding towards our Christian brothers, which in my case was tested almost immediately on all three counts when Arthur Ramsbottom whispered to me that he had left all his music at home and could he share with me. I really don't know what was worse: the pungency of his medicated sweet of which I got a whiff every time he opened his mouth to sing over my shoulder, or the subsequent raucous assault on my eardrums. The preacher went on for so long that the vicar decided to cut the anthem which we had been working on for the past two weeks, and because there was no communion today, there was no chance to insert the anthem anywhere else. Tripplehorn stormed into the vestry afterwards and exclaimed "Blasted Methodists don't know when to stop. That's the last year he preaches in this church." So much for Christian unity for another year.

Monday 21st January

I happened to bump into Margaret Pardew in town. She's been away from the choir because of a prolonged bout of flu but seemed quite cheerful today for one with an existence devoted to tending a sick mother and with as much dress sense as a potted cactus. She told me that she's trying to rustle up a group of five or six choir members to sing in a united service that's being hosted by the evangelical church on Wednesday night. It's rather short notice but, still feeling far from accepted amongst a significant number of choir members, I said I'd do it. The suggestion is we meet at 6.15 for a rehearsal which gives me precisely 45 minutes to get home, freshen up, force some food down me and then drive to the other end of town. Later I happened to see the perennially miserable Irving Cattermole and asked if he'd be joining us, to which he replied he would "rather skateboard across an alligator swamp in Nicaragua." I'd buy his ticket tomorrow.

Wednesday 23rd January

I managed to leave work slightly early and by dint of a microwave meal and a hair-raising drive somewhat in excess of the speed limit, I made it to the church, an unassuming modern building in the middle of a suburban housing estate, with a minute to spare. Margaret was standing outside, in an outfit that might have come straight from the special Wartime Austerity edition of *Women's Weekly*, announcing she was unable to get in. We stood cooling our heels for a good fifteen minutes until a young bearded man dressed somewhat incongruously in a thick hooded coat, long shorts and gym shoes, approached, exclaimed "Praise the Lord! Our St Basil's minstrels!", unlocked the front door and ushered us in. I asked Margaret who else was coming and she said "Rachel and Brian. That was all I could get hold of." At that moment Rachel appeared, apologising profusely for her lateness and advising us that Brian had been delayed at work and wouldn't be with us till gone seven at the very earliest. We agreed there was little point in rehearsing without him, so just stood there like a trio of spare dinners, watching as various people made their entrance. We noticed they were carrying a variety of containers and bags, and when I asked why was told "Oh, there's food first." This was most unwelcome news, for me at least; having had a large meal before coming out, I certainly felt in no mood to eat again for a while, and if we started too late I wouldn't get home in time to see who'd won tonight's big televised football match.

By 7.30, when the event was due to start, Brian still hadn't arrived, we hadn't sung a note, and there was a grand total of 17 people in the building. Before the meal we asked God's blessing on those who'd decided to stay away tonight. I wondered if we ought also to be praying for the producers of the TV football which I suspected was the real reason they'd done so. By 7.45, when I found myself drawn into an interminable conversation with a greasy-haired spotty young man in his early twenties named Duane over a slice of quite revolting curried quiche, I wondered if perhaps the multitude of absentees ought to be praying for me.

It was decided that owing to Brian's continued absence, our musical contribution – Attwood's *Teach Me O Lord* – should slot in not at the start of the act of worship as planned but roughly halfway through the meeting, which was scheduled to begin at half past eight. No sign of Brian even then, and I was all for suggesting we packed it in, but as everyone was taking their places for the meeting – at ten to nine – Margaret announced that she had secured the services of Angie, one of the singers in their own band, to take the tenor part if I would go down to bass. I suggested we ought to rehearse first, but Angie explained she was leading the opening part of the worship. "I'm sure the Lord has it all in hand," she said.

It was ten to ten, more than three and a half hours after arriving at the church, and following a whole sequence of prayers, testimonies and readings in no particular order, that it was finally suggested it might be nice to "hear what our good friends from St Basil's have to offer us." I suspect that a quartet of Mongolian yaks with laryngitis would probably have sung it better than we did, but incredibly, as we finished what was a travesty of a performance, the other 13 members applauded and muttered "Thank you, oh thank you so much, that was just beautiful," at such length and with such passion that I honestly wondered if we'd not just delivered a flawless rendition of Bach's *Mass in B minor* with the Academy of St Martin in the Fields. At this point I got up to leave, but Angie asked if I would "just stay for the final blessing." Suffice it to say that it was a good twenty minutes later that the meeting was drawn to a close and we all dispersed. As we were leaving, with no chance now of catching even the penalty shoot-out, Margaret rushed up to me, screeched "Thank you so much, you saved my life" and planted a huge wet kiss on my cheek. I didn't wait around for my curried-quiche-flavoured snog from Duane.

Friday 25th January
No Jane at choir tonight. No Margaret either. Tripplehorn seemed to know all about Wednesday night's debacle, commenting that Margaret had "about as much organising ability as a bucket of cold rice pudding." He then spent over half of the practice working on the Candlemas anthem we are performing, taken from the third section of the new anthem book. After we'd run through it for I think the fourteenth time, he announced that "it's now up to about a quarter of the standard I would expect from a class of backward six-year-olds." Lesley Markwick of course thought that was hilarious. Over coffee I asked her how Jane was, and she replied "She and Elliott are fine." "Oh, so it's back on again now, is it?" I laughed, remembering the conversation we'd had eight days ago. She gave me a strange look and said "Oh, no. You're thinking of Oliver. Elliott's her latest. Her third in two weeks to be exact. Slightly below average for her." Yet it seems only

yesterday that she was co-leader of the church youth group and twanging her guitar to songs of prayer for inner wholeness and purity in the Spirit.

While we were talking, one of the regular members of the congregation, Harriet Balfour, came into the church in some distress and asked to speak to Tripplehorn privately. A few minutes later they emerged, she sobbing her heart out, he placing a tender arm round her shoulder, and together they walked slowly to the door where he gave her a loving embrace. It was a genuinely touching sight. The moment the door had shut behind her, though, Tripplehorn walked briskly back up the nave, rubbed his hands and asked "Anyone for a funeral ten thirty Tuesday? Old Charles Balfour's finally popped his clogs. Not before time. Couple of hymns, coffee and sticky buns after." That man really has more faces than Madame Tussaud's waxworks.

Sunday 27th January – *THIRD SUNDAY AFTER EPIPHANY – SEPTUAGESIMA SUNDAY*

Some measure of divine reward for my endeavours last Wednesday night when I was informed that Arthur Ramsbottom had a bad cold and wouldn't be coming this morning. I was therefore able to enjoy not only a better sing but also more room in the tenor stalls.

The vicar was preaching elsewhere this morning and we had to put up with a retired priest who occasionally visits us, for our sins – in every sense. He announced our anthem as "The Lord Is Nowhere Among Us" rather than *The Lord Is Now Here Among Us* and preached drearily. I found a welcome distraction in an old hymn book that was lying on a little shelf immediately to the right of where Arthur Ramsbottom usually sits. Inside were a number of intriguing documents, including a wedding order of service dating back some fifty years, and a piece of paper giving details of a choir outing to Margate (*children, bring bucket and spade plus money for ice creams and donkey rides, make sure you give your 1/6 to Mrs Fazackerley*). So absorbed was I by this splendid fragment of choir history that the third hymn was being played over before I'd turned up the right page in the book, and there was no time to replace the old hymn book properly. Following the hymn there were intercessions including a period of silence in honour of victims of war crime. It was unfortunate that the old hymn book should choose that most poignant moment of the service to topple from the ledge on which I had hastily shoved it, and fall to the ground with a deafening crash.

Afterwards Alison Sparkes rounded on Matthew, said to him "How dare you drop books on the floor during the service," and gave him a smart clip round the ear. Despite his cries of pain and protests of innocence I kept silent. It was all Arthur Ramsbottom's fault anyway.

23

Monday 28th January

I had a call from West Shires this morning inviting me to their offices at lunchtime where they had some "good news" for me. I suppose it was naïve of me to hope it was a £10,000 windfall for being their thirty millionth satisfied customer, but on arrival it was still an anticlimax to be advised that my account had now been adjusted to the correct amount as a member of staff did recall my depositing the sum of £50 with them. To celebrate the receipt of a brand new passbook with the choir's name now correctly spelt, and bearing a computer entry that confirmed my credit balance, I decided to draw a fiver out and treat the choir to some really good coffee from the specialist retailer next door. I could almost sense the luscious aromas of Monsoon Malabar, Spicy Old Brown Java, Pico Duarte and Blue Mountain Jamaican. "Oh, I'm terribly sorry, sir," the clerk replied, "Because we only correctly credited your account this morning, you have to allow seven working days' clearance."

So Handysave Economy Instant it is for another week then.

Tuesday 29th January

A meeting I had planned for this morning couldn't go ahead, so I decided to go along to Charles Balfour's funeral using some time I had owing . Tripplehorn delighted to see me. "It's just Cora, Queenie and you," he said. "Take your choice – alto, tenor or bass. Or join the sops if you like. God knows they need all the help they can get." I was quite looking forward to flitting between the underneath parts, and before we went in I even found myself chatting reasonably amiably with Queenie on such weighty philosophical matters as the state of her husband's ingrowing toenail and the cost of sending an antique carriage clock to her cousin on the Isle of Dogs. A few minutes before the service, however, Tripplehorn came marching back in to the vestry in a fury. "You wouldn't believe this," he said, "but the priest's said we've got to sing Walford Davies' *God Be In My Head*. They might have told me." He proceeded to fling open the door of the music cupboard and rummaged frantically inside it for a good five minutes, sheets of paper flying through the air on a scale unwitnessed by me since my days in Form 3A and the legendary paper dart battle during Mr Pauncefoot's Latin class. Eventually he found the copies, threw them down on the table, and barked "There's no time to practise the blasted thing, just bone up on it during the sermon. I'm sure the priest will blabber on for long enough."

His prophecy proved to be spot on, for the eulogy delivered by the visiting priest, a bluff Yorkshireman who announced himself as team vicar of Acaster Malbis (wherever that may be), seemed endless. During what was in

24

reality a twenty-minute oration he touched upon every aspect of the life of Charles Balfour, from his penchant for standing knee-deep in mud on the Cambridgeshire Fens training his binoculars for sight of the marsh pipit and great-crested grebe, to his outstanding contribution to the Allerton Mauleverer Steak & Kidney Pudding Scoffers Anonymous. I was able to take a close look at the alto, tenor and bass parts, and decided, by way of variety, to do a bit of each. What I hadn't reckoned on was Queenie taking it upon herself to attempt a spot of alto singing, and the result was painful to say the least. Following a succession of discordant clashes between the two of us, Tripplehorn upped the organ accompaniment and in doing so pressed down so hard on the E flat above Middle C that it stuck and continued to register throughout the rest of the piece and the first half of the ensuing tape recording – somewhat inappositely, Simon & Garfunkel's *Sound Of Silence.*
I think the next time an office meeting is cancelled, I'll do something a little more relaxing. Like riding a unicycle backwards along the middle lane of the M25 dressed only in a pair of purple underpants.

Thursday 31st January
I got a call from Joan Trumpington at 6.50 this morning, believe it or not, saying she was in the course of sorting and cataloguing choir music and was desperately searching for spare copies of *Six Hundred Hymns For All*, or indeed photostat copies of pages from the book. What she could have wanted it for at ten to seven in the morning I can't begin to guess. But it is a most useful book with several excellent tunes that can't be found elsewhere, and indeed it would certainly be handy to have my own, particularly if copies are as hard to come by as Joan Trumpington suggests.
As it happened, this morning I was at a meeting in a neighbouring town which boasted an excellent music shop. I parked outside and went in, and by a miracle I saw a copy on the shelf, with an attractive colour cover. I seized the moment, grabbed the copy and proferred it, together with my debit card, at the counter. The rather geriatric assistant looked on the front and back covers of the book, and inside, but was quite unable to find a price. As a result, he had to make a lengthy telephone call following which he informed me that the book cost £35. "That can't be right," I protested. I pointed to another, much thicker, hymn book alongside it which was retailing for half that amount. "Just a moment," the assistant said, and turned to a catalogue under the counter. Ten minutes later he announced that according to the catalogue, the book should retail at £45. I suppose in the circumstances I should be grateful that he gave me the benefit of the doubt and charged me £35 after all. Even this victory was somewhat pyrrhic, however, for I finally

emerged into the daylight to find a traffic warden slapping a £30 parking ticket on my windscreen. As I approached him he turned to me, gave me a friendly smile and said "Oh, that's all right," which I assumed meant he was going to let me off. I was about to thank him profusely, but before I could do so he announced "I'll let you have it instead." Whereupon he picked up the ticket, shoved it into my hand, and walked off.

Tripplehorn rang me this evening wanting to check I'd be there tomorrow because owing to absences in the ranks he was having second thoughts about our special Candlemas anthem. Having said I would indeed be present, I told him of my new purchase. "It was a bit dear," I said. "Thirty five quid." He replied "You should have asked me. I've got about ten kicking around at home. I'd have given you one for nothing. In fact, I'd have paid you to take the lot off my hands." Perhaps I should. It might pay for the parking ticket.

FEBRUARY

Friday 1st February

Made my way to choir in excellent spirits tonight, looking forward to a day's shopping in London tomorrow. We spent a long time looking at Sunday's psalm, and it was well after eight when we turned our attention to the Candlemas anthem. After four fairly dire runs through it, Tripplehorn turned irritably from the organ stool and said "It's obvious this is nowhere near performance standard and I've got a lot more to get through tonight. Is there anyone who can't come back early afternoon tomorrow for an extra practice?" Alison Sparkes raised her hand, as did her children, and I raised mine – whereupon Tripplehorn threw the anthem book down on the floor and said "That's it, then. Not enough men. We can't do it." For the rest of the practice he was in an absolutely foul mood, threatening to walk out himself on a couple of occasions, but I refused to give in. As I whispered to Rachel Ellis, who I know isn't the greatest fan of our choirmaster at the best of times, "I really don't see why he should make me out to be the guilty party. I'm not going to be emotionally blackmailed and that's that." She nodded sagely and said "Don't let him bully you."

Which made it even more incomprehensible that half an hour later I should emerge, having not only sacrificed my day in London to attend the extra practice, but agreed to make coffee and tea for everyone before the start of the rehearsal by way of a peace offering for giving up a free afternoon, and lock up when we'd finished. While Rachel looked on sadly at me as if to ask why I had not gone the whole hog and invited the whole choir back to my house afterwards for a champagne reception and seven-course meal followed by a firework extravaganza and a marching display from the Fourteenth East Smethwick Drum Majorettes.

Sunday 3rd February – *CANDLEMAS*

A somewhat nerve-wracking service in prospect today, not only because of the difficult anthem, which had indeed taken up a substantial proportion of yesterday afternoon, but the fact that for much of the service, including the anthem, we were holding lighted candles. We were advised that we could extinguish the candles after the anthem had been sung. We sang the anthem extremely well – I even saw Tripplehorn do a "thumbs-up" sign from the organ – but even after I'd tried to blow the flame of my candle out, the wick continued to exhibit a small glow whilst giving out such large quantities of smoke that Eileen Crosby burst into an uncontrollable fit of coughing. Further blowing failed to extinguish the flame, so in my desperation I stubbed out the wick on the final page of the anthem we'd just been singing, creating a huge black blob which obliterated the tenor and bass parts for bars 145 to 147. Matthew Sparkes spotted it, and presumably in revenge for what had happened last Sunday, he made sure everybody knew afterwards. I felt constrained to interrupt Joan Trumpington in the middle of her misfiling the copies of this morning's mass setting to ask what I should do. "It's Mr Tripplehorn you'll have to answer to," she said, "but those books are £14.95 each and we have had a choir policy for many years that members must replace defaced copies at their own expense. You'll have to speak to him, but I'm sure that's what he'll say."

Decided to go and see him at once, only to find he'd left, and thirteen attempts to phone him during the afternoon failed to yield a response. By the time *Songs Of Praise* had come on TV at tea-time, I had got myself frantic with worry, wondering if in fact a simple payment of £14.95 would be sufficient or whether I would have to undergo some additional punishment: another Saturday afternoon detention, perhaps, or being chained to one of the choirstalls while choir members pelted rotten eggs and brandished Oriental disembowelling cutlasses at me to the accompaniment of Cora Willoughby-Smith's unique interpretation of *Where The Bee Sucks*.

I finally got hold of him at nine that night. When I told him what had happened he merely said "That anthem was getting on my nerves by the time we did it. You might torch all the other copies while you're about it." I told him what Joan Trumpington had said about the choir policy, and he replied laughingly "We stopped doing that years ago. Take no notice of the silly old bat." Yet to think that on top of her normal secretarial duties, she'd been up till one this morning to finish the cataloguing of all the choir music at his request, and barely eight weeks ago she'd single-handedly prised him from the organ seat after some prankster had smeared superglue on it. That's gratitude for you.

Friday 8th February

Found a lovely Valentine card for Jane Markwick at lunchtime. It depicted two singing cats and the message inside was "Let's make beautiful mewsic." Corny, but not over-sentimental and totally appropriate.

A shorter practice tonight because Tripplehorn wanted to talk to us about what as far as he is concerned are the three biggest choir events during the year. Two sound excellent: the choir concert, to be held in late May, and a recording session to take place in the autumn. The idea, I believe, is to print CD's and tapes to be sold as Christmas gifts and raise money for the church roof. My heart sank as he announced that the third event, which he wishes to take place in mid-April, is a Herbert Bumfrey Workshop, to raise funds for the church roof. He thinks he can assemble together sufficient material to make a full day and plans to invite not only other local church choirs and musicians but also representatives from the media. He says he has a contact at Classic FM that might be interested. Lesley Markwick got very excited about this but I don't think she should lose any sleep over it. The last time I heard someone in the musical world boasting of a contact in Classic FM it turned out to be a cleaner who'd just emigrated to Bangladesh. I can't imagine the take-up from other musicians is going to be enormous either. Perhaps someone, myself maybe as the one who inadvertently gave him the idea in the first place, ought to mention that we are here talking about a composer whose setting of all two verses of Psalm 117 runs to twelve pages. Plus a repeat.

We were asked to nominate pieces we might like to include in the choir concert. Lesley's request for Mendlessohn's *Hear My Prayer* went down well, as did Irving Cattermole's suggestion of Brahms' *How Lovely Are Thy Dwellings* and Alison Sparkes' request for Mozart's *Ave Verum*. My suggestion of Bumfrey's setting of all 176 verses of Psalm 119 less ecstatically received.

To round off the practice, we sang *God So Loved The World* from Stainer's *Crucifixion*, in preparation for the performance of this work which the choir traditionally gives on Palm Sunday. This particular chorus is also likely to find its way into the concert, being a firm favourite with many, myself included. Those wonderful words from John 3: "....that he gave his only begotten Son that whoso believeth in Him should not perish but have everlasting life" send goose-pimples up my spine every time. We ran aground on the words "gave his only begotten Son" prompting Zoe Sparkes to enquire of her mother what "begotten" meant. I was quite unable to make head or tail of Alison's explanation but it seemed to shut Zoe up which presumably was the main thing. I'm only grateful Alison wasn't asked about "Everlasting Life." I wouldn't have put it past her to tell her daughter that it's the name of that new insurance company in Rope Walk.

Sunday 10th February – *FOURTH SUNDAY AFTER EPIPHANY* – *QUINQUAGESIMA*

Arrived at church to be told that Tripplehorn was ill in bed with the flu. Irving Cattermole, who normally fills in on such occasions, was also away, and Mr Saigeman from the Baptist Church was to be playing for us instead. Before the service, he warned us "I'm only really used to playing hymns out of the *Baptist Hymn Book*" and judging by the dreadful mess he made of the processional hymn, I wondered if his repertoire even in that volume was restricted to hymns with a key signature of no more than one sharp or one flat and minimal need to deviate from the white notes on the keyboard. Fortunately the psalm was only six verses, but that was still probably six verses too many for Mr Saigeman. We moved on to the gradual hymn, *Lord Enthroned In Heavenly Splendour*, where from the play-over it was clear he was playing the wrong tune. By some miracle, however, the tune he played did actually fit the words, and the vicar managed to work this strangely providential happening into the sermon, on the subject of serendipity, suggesting that it may all have been pre-planned anyway. Less obviously pre-ordained by divine hands was Mr Saigeman's play-over for *Living Lord* from which it became clear that he understood the chosen tune to be that for *Praise To The Lord The Almighty The King Of Creation*. And only those of a very radical theological and philosophical persuasion would fathom why, when the time came for the anthem – Pitoni's *Cantate Domino* – Mr Saigeman should have in front of him the music for the somewhat unseasonal *Christmas Is Coming, The Geese Are Getting Fat*. Especially as the anthem was actually unaccompanied. Fortunately Ken Foulkes, who I imagine was half expecting something of this sort, leaned over Mr Saigeman's shoulder, produced the necessary chord on the organ, and conducted the anthem himself. In a way I was quite disappointed.

We were reminded afterwards that as many of us as possible are requested to form a choir on Ash Wednesday this week. Mr Saigeman sadly cannot be with us. Pity. I am sure we would be the first miserable penitents to have received the ashes on our foreheads and given the sober reminder of our mortality and need for forgiveness before God, to the strains of *Didn't We Have A Loverly Time The Day We Went To Bangor*.

Wednesday 13th February *– ASH WEDNESDAY*
Having been told in church on Sunday that attendance at church tonight for the sung mass with litany and imposition of ashes with address by Archie Ainscow the sometime rural dean of Stansted Mountfitchet was more or less obligatory, I was somewhat nonplussed to enter the church from the vestry a the start of the service to find a congregation of precisely four. But as our vicar put it somewhat irreverently during the welcome, "that just makes all the more ashes to go round." The reduced numbers certainly did not set the adrenalin pumping, and it was hardly surprising, in the lack-lustre atmosphere, that concentration was not what it should have been. Hence the slight misunderstanding at the end of *Forty Days And Forty Nights*, which we sang unaccompanied. I had understood the final note in the tenor part

was to be sharpened; Craig Dumbleton unfortunately had not, and sang a note a semitone lower, while Arthur Ramsbottom hovered somewhere in between the two of us. I could see Tripplehorn wasn't happy with the resultant discordant melee. I know of nobody who registers displeasure with the back of their head as effectively as he does.

Rachel asked afterwards if I'd like to come straight back to her house for an "extra pancake party." Apparently she'd had a Shrove Tuesday celebration yesterday but there was so much mixture left over she said she felt it'd be more of an offence in the Lord's eyes to waste it than tuck in on a day of supposed abstinence and self-denial. I heartily agreed. As we were enjoying our theologically inappropriate banquet, Brian was telling me all about his son's new PC, which he'd had installed just before Christmas and which can actually print music. I can't say I'm not tempted myself, and told Brian so. I've always regretted that it was for want of legibility that my very own setting of *Old MacDonald Had A Farm* failed to find favour with the Wolverhampton Polytechnic glee club.

I was thinking about leaving, after my sixth pancake, when Lesley and Jane appeared. Jane looked totally stunning and gave me a really beaming smile. As she waited for her pancake we enjoyed a lovely conversation and suddenly she tugged at my sleeve and asked if she could talk to me privately. I was excited. Had she received the Valentine, guessed it was from me, and decided to pursue me instead of Elliott? She ushered me into the empty dining room, closed the door behind her, burst out laughing and said "Did you know you had a dirty great smudge all over your forehead?" before promptly walking back out to the kitchen to eat her pancake.

So much for the beautiful mewsic.

Friday 15th February

Tonight we received details of the Come And Praise Convention which is to be held in a big church in South London on the 16th of next month. We will be one of a massed band of some 40 choirs from across the south. No mention thankfully of burger bars or portable latrines, although we have been advised to bring food to supplement the teas and coffees that will be provided. It's all been arranged through Margaret Pardew, whose brother is one of the principal organisers. The aim of the event is to "bring the good news to the community through music," and will involve contributions from many different choirs. During the day there will be various workshops and seminars, with contributions by each choir, representing a broad spectrum of Christian music-making. The climax of the event will be a big "praise party" in the evening with, as the accompanying literature puts it, a "constant

stream of joyous songs to the Lord." Because of lack of parking – and presumably also because of the amount of car crime in the area – it's suggested we park on the outskirts of London and then use public transport the rest of the way. It does sound an awfully long day. I asked Margaret, who had all the details, how long into the evening it was likely to last, but all she could say was "It's in the Lord's hands."
I only hope the Lord knows the time of the last train from Balham.

Sunday 17th February – *FIRST SUNDAY IN LENT*
A larger congregation than usual, a combination perhaps of the start of Lent with a visit from members of an organisation announcing itself as the North Burundi Full Gospel Business Men's Fellowship. Whatever that may be.
Having spoken a modern version of the words of the Litany on Ash Wednesday, the vicar was this morning asking us to process round the church while singing the Prayer Book Litany. This involved singing the words "Good Lord, deliver us" eight times, and "We beseech thee to hear us, good Lord" no fewer than twenty-one times, in response to a series of sung petitions by the vicar. The responses had been composed by Percy Luffington, a former choirmaster of St Basil's. They weren't that straightforward but as Tripplehorn told us, "at least you'll have plenty of chances to get them right." Yet I think it was only once we'd got to number 16 of 21 that we were singing them as the good Dr Luffington intended, and Queenie Haverthwaite was still struggling with the tricky A flat on the word "good." At least I think it was number 16, as the words to be sung by the priest weren't included in our music. We were told simply to continue to sing "We beseech thee to hear us, good Lord" until we heard the priest sing the magic words "Son of God, we beseech thee to hear us" whereupon we were to echo these words and the litany would then conclude with two verses and the responses "Grant us thy peace." Unfortunately, no sooner had we heard the magic words and responded accordingly than the vicar launched into a petition which from my vague memories of rehearsing it on Friday should have been one of the 21 requiring the "We beseech thee" response. I assume the vicar had just forgotten to sing it earlier, although I honestly don't know how many people would have noticed if it had already been intoned three or even four times. None of us really had any idea what to do next. It didn't help, in the context of making a decision, that we were still marching dutifully round the building, now on our third lap and thereby getting our third opportunity to study Mrs Robertson's varicose veins, inhale the tobacco-raddled breath of Mr Briggs and trip over the umbrella which Miss Bullivant had carelessly dropped into our collective paths. Tripplehorn

saved the situation by robustly playing over the tune for the first hymn, which according to the order of service wasn't supposed to be sung until after the first reading. I think it's what is called reactive management, but none of us really quite knew what to make of it. Least of all, judging by the looks on their faces, the North Burundi Full Gospel Business Men's Fellowship.

Monday 18th February

Had a phone call from Ken Foulkes this evening. He really is a nice man; he's a good singer and yet is always so modest and unassuming. His exquisite solo part in *Three Kings From Persian Lands Afar* has become a real tradition of the Christmas worship at St Basil's, and long may it remain so. He asked me if I'd like to join with a number of other choir members in singing at a wedding in a neighbouring church in June and I said I'd be delighted. He then said "Rumour has it that you're wanting to buy a PC to print out music." I told him that I was indeed, and was taking a day off on Wednesday to purchase it. "Well, I think it's a brilliant idea," he said. "I mean, I take it you know Tony Smart, one of our regular congregation? He owns a computer store in town and he'll do you an excellent deal." Come to think of it, I believe I had overheard Ken chatting to Tony on the subject over coffee after the service yesterday. He went on "Did you know that in our choir archives we've some absolute musical gems buried away. When we had that purge last month, I just stopped them being thrown out. Gathering dust for years, all torn, faded and virtually illegible. Frank Tripplehorn would have loved to keep them. If you were able to reprint them on computer, he'd be thrilled. So would I for that matter. You never know, this might become quite a lucrative sideline for you."

The conversation inspired me to go up to the loft in order to look out some of my own old music that I might transfer to computer once I've got it. In doing so, I came across my old glee club sweatshirt which I've not worn for years. Having been worn for many post-rehearsal pub sessions, it still exudes the aroma of cigarette smoke, but I think I might wear it at Friday's practice. While I'm not one to flaunt my past musical endeavours for the sake of scoring cheap points off my fellow choristers, I like to feel that being seen to have formerly associated with such an august assembly of performers must enhance my standing within my current choral community.

It is a pity that after three attempts at washing it I still can't get rid of the smell.

Wednesday 20th February

Over breakfast this morning I was reading my free local newspaper and saw an ad for PC's on offer at "unbelievable" prices at SupaComputa, a large warehouse-type establishment situated on the big complex on the edge of the town. Their PC's certainly seem a lot better value for money than those offered by Tony Smart, and though I know Tony to be a fine upstanding member of the church, there is little point in going to him if I can get the same product with SupaComputa at half the price. Accordingly, I decided to opt for SupaComputa for my new equipment.

Any illusions I might have had about being able to browse at leisure round the range of merchandise on offer were promptly shattered when a young man sporting a bright green shirt and a badge bearing the ominous words I'M DARREN – HAPPY TO HELP pounced on me the moment I came through the door, and before I could get as much as a word in edgeways he was extolling the virtues of a whole range of hardware and software, his speech liberally laced with computer terminology that was as intelligible to the uninitiated as a treatise in ancient Swahili on Avogadro's Hypothesis would be to a hibernating hedgehog. When he eventually ran out of steam I was able to tell him what I was actually after, prompting him to another bout of compu-verbal diarrhoea, but the outcome was that two hours after arriving, I found myself returning to my car wheeling a trolley on which was precariously balanced a new computer and printer, an array of software, and an instruction manual helpfully calling itself a Complete Idiot's Guide. And considerably poorer than I had been when I'd gone in.

Having felt quite optimistic about installing my computer without any assistance from outside, I had spurned Darren's offer for one of their specialist staff to do it for me at what seemed an exorbitant additional cost. It soon became clear, however, that the instruction manual was no more comprehensible than Darren's sales patter had been earlier in the day, and after three hours I was still no nearer to going live than I had been at the start. Eventually I admitted defeat and called Brian Ellis. Rachel answered and told me that Brian was going to be late home but would call me as soon as he got in. I had intended to treat myself to a night at the cinema but I was now so desperate to get the computer working that I decided to stay in and await his call. By ten he was still not in so I decided to have one very last go at it and if that failed I would go to bed.

As I crumpled up underneath the duvet, still no nearer to making it work, at twenty to two, I realised why the equipment had been accompanied by a Complete Idiot's Guide. Only a complete idiot would have bought it in the first place.

34

Thursday 21st February

Brian rang soon after I got in from work. "I gather you've got problems with your PC," he said. When I told him I had, and I hoped he could do for me what he'd done for his son and help me set up, he sighed and said "Oh, I didn't actually do the installation. I got my friend Phil Davis to install it. He's a real expert on computers. Nothing too much trouble – just makes it look so easy." " Sounds great," I said. "Where can I get hold of him?" "India, for the next six months," said Brian.

Friday 22nd February

I rang SupaComputa who've promised to come next Tuesday – at a cost of a hefty callout fee, payable by debit card up front, and a day off from work. They say the engineer will be round any time between ten and four thirty. "Which I assume means I'll see him at twenty eight minutes past four having waited in all day," I could not resist saying. But I might just as well have been trying to humour a Bosnian bus inspector during a blizzard.

From the moment I got to choir tonight I knew it was a mistake to wear the glee club sweatshirt, pong-free though it now was thanks to two more washes and a rather more powerful detergent. Henry Peasgood immediately said he should have brought along his Baltimore Barbershop Babes T-shirt, made specially for the appearance of the "Babes" on US network television, which has recently been repeated on a couple of UK cable channels. In the circumstances, it seemed best not to mention the glee club's only moment of media fame, to wit its two-minute recording for *Midlands Tonight* on the occasion of the tenth anniversary of the club's foundation – the slot subsequently cut to a five-second still to make more room for comment on the council's newly-published report on the environmental impact of pigeon droppings in West Bromwich. Zoe Sparkes was prompted to suggest that we ought to have a St Basil's Choir sweatshirt but I somehow can't see it. The difficulty is in finding one enormous enough to fit across Cora Willoughby-Smith's bust. Or get over Henry Peasgood's head.

Sunday 24th February – *SECOND SUNDAY IN LENT*

We did Allegri's *Miserere* today – a slightly edited version, with organ accompaniment and without the very high notes. I suppose we do still need to keep some of our glassware intact. Any attempt by Cora Willoughby-Smith to sing above top F and you could say goodbye to the east window.

John and Alex Adams were in church for the first time for some weeks. They are a lovely couple; I owe them a special debt of thanks because they put me up when I was house-hunting a few years ago. They also gave me a lot of support after Jackie upped and left me. They brought their baby twins Kirsten and Daisy who unfortunately throughout the Allegri kept up an almost unbroken screaming. Rather than take the children outside, Alex did her best to quell the noise, but to no avail.

We had a guest preacher this morning. In her sermon she gave a stark warning of the dire consequences for the future of a Church that was steeped in cliqueyness and made outsiders, especially the young, feel excluded and unloved. It obviously had a huge impact on Irving Cattermole who as we were leaving afterwards said "Could have done with a machine gun for those wretched kids during the Allegri, couldn't we?" In my view their top notes weren't actually that much out of tune with the organ. Which is more than could be said for the top F's of Cora Willoughby-Smith.

Tuesday 26th February

I nipped out at quarter to ten for a carton of milk and packet of tea bags in case the SupaComputa man needed any refreshment while he worked. As I was on my way back, Tripplehorn accosted me and asked me if I would sing the tenor solo for the Stainer on Palm Sunday, which I readily agreed to, and then went on to explain, at considerable length, that he has mailed every organist/choirmaster in the English-speaking world to advise them of the Herbert Bumfrey workshop on 13th April. As a result I arrived home again at two minutes after ten. On walking in I saw a card stuffed through the letterbox advising me that the computer engineer had called round to see me without success, and if I wanted to re-arrange the appointment I should telephone the number on the bottom of the card. Assuming the number to be the engineer's mobile, I rang to ask if it was too late for him to pop back to my house before he left the town completely. "What town would that be, sir?" he enquired. Somewhat surprised, I gave him my exact position, compass bearing and location, only for him to pronounce that he'd never heard of it. Now believing myself to be in a bad dream, I asked if I was in fact speaking to the SupaComputa store. "No, sir," he answered. "This is Associated Computers Help Line. In Kirkintilloch. Just outside Glasgow."

I explained to him what had happened and he promised he would sort it out and someone would get back to me as soon as possible. As any prudent customer would, I asked him for his name and direct line but he said there was little point in giving it to me as he would be finishing his shift very shortly and he would be passing the matter on to someone else. "Can you tell me who, then?" I asked him. "Not sure, to be honest," he said. "Could be Julie....no, she's rung in sick....Dawn perhaps....Tracy....or possibly Jo." "Is that a man or a woman?" I asked him. "I don't know," he replied.

Two hours later I had still heard nothing so I decided on a different tack and rang the local SupaComputa direct. "All I want to know," I said, "is whether the engineer who I just missed this morning can fit me in later in the day." "I'm afraid I can't tell you," was the response. "I can give you a number to call, and they'll look into it for you." Seconds later, I found myself writing down the number of the Associated Computers Help Line. In Kirkintilloch. Just outside Glasgow.

Decided to cut my losses and telephoned Andy Stubbs, an independent computer engineer in town who promised he'd try and get over some time during the afternoon, albeit at a cost considerably greater than the call-out fee charged by SupaComputa. He finally arrived at twenty past four, my mind now numbed by three hours' thumb-twiddling, window-watching and daytime TV. As he was working away, the doorbell rang again to reveal a man who said he'd been sent by SupaComputa. "So my calls to your Help Line obviously did the trick," I said. "I don't know about that," he said. "I've not had base speak to me at all today. I was on my way home and just popped by on the off chance."

With Andy Stubbs now on the case I decided to send him away. Whether I'll now be able to recover the fee I've already paid SupaComputa is anyone's guess, although a glance at the small print gives me no encouragement whatsoever.

An hour later Andy Stubbs had gone, having patiently written down every step necessary to turn me into a modern-day Scarlatti, and I was ready to start work on my very first piece of music. Or so I thought. Four more hours, and all I had to show for my efforts was approximately thirty-five sheets of A4 which bore as much resemblance to a piece of music as an EU practice direction on the handling of wet fish. There again, perhaps I had no right to expect any more of a machine that is serviced by individuals who don't know the sex of their own workmates.

Wednesday 27th February

Desperate situations call for desperate measures. I rang Tony Smart whose business I had so foolishly spurned a week ago. By the end of our conversation I'd eaten so much humble pie I'd got myself indigestion, but it was worth it, as Tony agreed to pop round after work. Less than two and a half hours after starting, he'd printed off an immaculate page of music, and, more to the point, explained exactly where Andy Stubbs and I had gone wrong yesterday. "He's a nice chap, Andy," Tony said charitably. "But with respect, computer engineering isn't his strong point. Just looks better on his

CV than his real job." "Which is?" I queried. "Second hand car salesman," he replied.

As he was leaving, having relieved me of only slightly less money than Mr Stubbs, he asked me how much I'd paid for the package, less the installation charges. When I told him, he whistled and said "I could have sold and installed exactly the same equipment for thirty per cent less. Church connection, you see. I discount any computer equipment I sell that's used for furthering the ministry of St Basil's. Call it my contribution to God's work, if you like. Never mind. Cheerio."

Sat down to watch TV in the hope that I might be cheered up by seeing someone give a wrong answer on *Who Wants To Be A Millionaire* and thereby lose even more thousands of pounds than I had succeeded in losing in the past seven days. Instead I found they were doing an in-depth investigation into rogue traders. To be precise, second hand car salesmen.

MARCH

Friday 1st March

With rain pouring from the sky all day, it was doubly unfortunate that the church path was being relaid this week and we had to paddle through liquid mud from the lychgate to the church door for tonight's choir practice.

A somewhat less demanding piece to practise for this Sunday's service than for last Sunday's, as we sang through Hilton's *Lord For Thy Tender Mercy's Sake*. After we'd rehearsed it for the fourth time, Matthew Sparkes started sniggering, and when Alison enquired what the joke was, he responded "It's the words on page 3, 'That we may walk with an upright tart!'"

Although Matthew's wit was merely rewarded with a sharp rebuke from his mother, and a reminder that the words were actually 'walk *in* an upright *heart*,' I noticed that she made no move to stop him plugging his ears when Cora Willoughby-Smith took it upon herself to sing the solo part in *O For The Wings Of A Dove* from Mendelssohn's *Hear My Prayer*, on which we concentrated during the latter part of the evening, with a view to singing it as an anthem next week and in the choir concert. Her efforts really were cringe-making. When she was out of earshot, Tripplehorn muttered words to the effect that he'd heard pleasanter sounds emanating from his pet budgie when it was castrated. Yet she's clearly determined to sing that solo in performance. This could be bloody.

Norah Duff, one of the church cleaners, came in towards the end and had a go at us for leaving our muddy footprints in the nave aisle after she'd spent all day cleaning it for tomorrow's wedding blessing. After she'd left, Henry Peasgood cried "Altogether now.... 'O for the whinge, for the whinge of a Duff!'"

"I'd rather have the upright tart," Tripplehorn muttered.

Sunday 3rd March – *THIRD SUNDAY IN LENT*

Matthew's contribution on Friday seemed to have had more of an impact than he could have dared to hope, since when it came to the anthem, half the choir did in fact sing 'walk *with* an upright heart.' And so poor was our enunciation, if anyone listening didn't know the words they would have concluded that we were indeed seeking to walk with upright tarts.

As we were disrobing afterwards, Margaret asked if those who were coming to the Come And Praise Convention in Balham could remain behind for a runthrough of the pieces we're doing that day. This was the first inkling I'd had that attendance was purely voluntary rather than it being a full choir event. Having been looking for some sort of pretext to get out of it, I seized the moment. "I'm sorry, I don't think I'm going to be able to make it," I told her, trying hard to assume an expression of one burdened by grave responsibility rather than one cheesed off at missing a weekend evening in front of the box. Her face dropped faster than an express lift full of overweight elephants. "Oh dear," she said. "In that case I think the whole thing may be a non-starter. We've had all the arrangements in place for months, as well." I decided I was not going to become the make-or-break factor in yet another choir event, so I said to her slightly mischievously "I believe the Lord has other uses for me that day." Queenie Haverthwaite's eyes lit up. "Oh, good," she said. "Hazel Ledworthy's obviously asked you. I knew she was desperate for an extra pair of hands on the ladies' lingerie stall at the St Basil's Nearly New sale."

I suppose Balham isn't exactly the end of the universe. And Saturday night TV's never been quite the same since the demise of Dusty Bin.

Wednesday 6th March

The post brought a letter to all those taking part in the Come And Praise Convention advising us that there's to be a regional rehearsal for the event next Wednesday night, fifty miles away. I can't think of anything worse. Also a letter from West Shires Building Society telling me that unless I clear my £150 arrears with them, my home is at risk. I had the greatest pleasure in ripping it into tiny pieces and bucking the trend towards global warming by creating my very own snowstorm on my back patio.

Tripplehorn rang me this evening and confided in me that he's asking Samantha Ashton, one of his singing pupils from the technical college to come and sing the Mendelssohn on Sunday and again at the concert. I asked if Cora knew this was happening, and he said "She will on Friday."

So it's war.

Friday 8th March

I arrived at the practice more or less on time and heard a quite exquisite soprano voice echoing round the church. For a moment I wondered if angels were present – there are at least six well documented accounts of angels being seen in St Basil's – but it was in fact a girl, looking no more than fifteen or sixteen, singing the Mendelssohn. Samantha Ashton, I presume. I also heard agitated voices from the vestry, and a glance in that direction confirmed that they belonged to Cora Willoughby-Smith, Joan Trumpington and Hazel Ledworthy. A scary sight indeed. Still, now I know why the church has always been blissfully free from break-ins. An intruder seeing them together would run a mile.

40

Moments later, I saw Tripplehorn heading for the vestry, and the door was shut firmly behind him. For the next twenty minutes the rest of us sat uncomfortably in the stalls, making desultory conversation but aware that Armageddon was brewing just yards away from us. Matthew was all for going to have a closer listen. I can see he has a career lined up as either a comedian or a *News Of The World* reporter. Possibly both.

At length our choirmaster emerged, followed by the formidable triumvirate. Further whispered conversations and mutterings later, Samantha was seen to be making a hasty exit, and when the time came for *Hear My Prayer*, Cora W.S. was taking centre stage again, setting about the Mendlessohn with all the grace and finesse of a roller-blading rhinoceros.

Later on in the pub, Craig Dumbleton was able to pass on what he had gleaned, third or possibly fourth hand, over coffee while I had been busy emptying the urn. "I think Frank could just about have survived Joan resigning as choir secretary and librarian, Hazel as member of the PCC not pressing for any more funds for the purchase of new music and choir robes, and Cora refusing to offer the use of her house for the choir summer party," he said. "What really broke him was their joint resolution to make it their business not to let him win, for the sixth year running, the £10 gardening voucher in the church garden show's rudest looking vegetable competition."

Am not sure whether to take him seriously or not. One can never entirely feel at ease with the verbal utterances of one who claims to know the opening hours of every railway station booking office on the line between Fenchurch Street and Shoeburyness.

Sunday 10th March – *MOTHERING SUNDAY*

A glorious sunny morning, and an excellent congregation for the special Mothering Sunday service. Before the service the vicar spoke to us about the Passiontide services. We're being asked to provide a choir on Maundy Thursday at 7.30pm and Good Friday at 2pm, but there is no service this year on Holy Saturday evening – this decision doubtless influenced by the fact that last year's Holy Saturday service lasted from 9pm until 11.45pm and by the end there was a congregation of two. Instead, the vicar's trying a new idea – a sunrise service with full choir incorporating much of the Holy Saturday liturgy and starting at 5.30am on Easter Sunday morning. When I expressed doubts as to whether that would increase the congregation at all, let alone get it into the hoped-for double figures, the vicar replied "It's being well publicised, I can assure you. Father O'Flaherty is putting a couple of lines in the Our Lady Of Sorrows weekly bulletin, and Simon Phelan's promised to mention it in his *What's On In Church* slot on Rustic FM. At seven thirty on Sunday morning, repeated at ten thirty on Sunday night." Wow. I hope we've notified the police and lined up a force of crowd control stewards.

Today's service was a simpler and shorter form of worship than usual. Sadly my own mother passed away some years ago but it was touching, all the same, to see Matthew and Zoe go up to fetch posies for Alison, and Jane do the same for Lesley. Appropriately enough for Mothering Sunday, Cora gave the mother of all hashed renditions of *Hear My Prayer*, coming in two bars too early and mis-hitting at least eight notes in the first two lines. I gave up counting after that. Over coffee and simnel cake afterwards I got talking to a newly-married couple visiting St Basil's for the first time. "Lovely service," the husband said. "Though if I may say so, perhaps you might have thought about asking one of the music students from the tech to sing the solo. Very talented, some of them. Punters would love it. Why not suggest it to your choirmaster?" Perhaps I will. The next time I fancy having my head hacked off and used as a dish mop.

Wednesday 13th March

Margaret rang me early to offer me a lift to tonight's convention rehearsal which her brother Mike was leading. I'd understood I was taking Rachel and Brian but Margaret told me they'd had to drop out. This just left Margaret, Queenie, Craig and myself, and Margaret decided she could fit us all into her car. Before we left I asked her "You sure you know where we're going?" She smiled and responded "The Lord will guide us." I suppose that ought to have reassured me and I felt quite ashamed that it didn't. Until we arrived on the outskirts of the town and completed six laps of its outer ring road system, cutting up a Ford Mondeo on the third circuit and nearly squashing a cyclist on our fifth. I was all for going home, as it was now ten past seven and we were supposed to have started at six thirty. Eventually, with the assistance of a local wino and the policeman who'd flagged us down for driving the wrong way round the Goat and Compasses roundabout, we did track the hall down, to find we weren't an hour late as we thought but half an hour early. I decided there and then that I would find a pretext to travel to London independently on Saturday.

There were quite a few people there but in true Anglican fashion, the front three rows of seats were empty. Margaret said "Mike has a nasty habit of coming in and moving all the empty seats at the front." Accordingly I suggested we positioned ourselves right at the back, and we were sitting quite anonymously and happily when Mike walked in and said "Why are you all facing the wrong way?" To our horror, we found ourselves turning our seats round so we were right at the front. Any thoughts I might have had about slipping away in search of an early train home or catching up with the unfinished portion of the *Times* crossword were swiftly banished. I don't know what I found more excruciating – interminable repetition of choruses the arrangements of which would have insulted the intelligence of a dyslexic anteater, or being directly under the gaze of a leader whose armpits smelt as though they'd last been washed when Maggie Thatcher was in Downing Street and whose sandalled feet exuded the aroma of a sweaty gorgonzola cheese.

We were fortunately done by twenty past nine but Margaret again managed to get lost in her attempts to convey us out of the town. It can't have helped her concentration that she insisted on playing, at full blast, a cassette featuring some of the music we'd been working on that evening. When one particularly repetitive track came to an end, the final chord virtually drowned out on the tape by wild applause and cheering, Margaret cried excitedly "That really is a little foretaste of heaven." One suspects that writers such as Bunyan, Spenser and Dante, who fashioned their own exquisite images of the hereafter, would be mightily disappointed if heaven really was going to consist of listening to second-rate recordings of musical works of mind-numbing banality whilst performing endless circuits of an inner-ring road system with nothing more exciting to behold than pay and display carparks, cut-price carpet warehouses and scrap metal depositories.

Friday 15th March

Margaret came up to me at the end of tonight's rehearsal and told me something dreadful had happened. For one wonderful moment I thought she was going to tell me tomorrow was off. No such good fortune. She was simply telling me that she couldn't give me a lift as she was staying the night with her brother in Camberwell. Ever the diplomat, I told her "I quite understand, Margaret. It's really no problem" whereupon she threw her arms round me and said "You are an absolute darling. I've worried myself sick all afternoon about how you'd take the news. Thank you so much!" Afterwards in the pub, Rachel elbowed me in the ribs and said "I love a bit of in-choir romance," reminded me that there hadn't been a wedding between two choir members at St Basil's before but "you and young Margaret would make a lovely couple."

Somehow after that, watching the late-night movie on BBC2, dubbed by one critic "the scariest picture I've ever seen," seemed an anticlimax.

Saturday 16th March

Despite the fact that it was a filthy morning, after three consecutive days' rain, I actually found myself feeling quite good about the day as I set off. Our "regional" choir was not actually performing until around four thirty which gave me the opportunity to go into central London first and make a bit of a day of it. I managed to park in a residential street by a green very close to the church, reasoning that my vehicle was just as vulnerable further out of the city as it was here. I was determined to get away no later than eight, whatever stage the proceedings were at.

A busy few hours' shopping followed, including some more software for my PC which will enable me to incorporate illustrations into the music I print out, and a CD of Stainer's *Crucifixion*.

I arrived in the community centre attached to the church at twenty past four to find a centre packed with people, and an atmosphere which at once seemed positive and uplifting. I was warmly welcomed by a middle-aged couple who told me that the main hall was being used for the regional choir contributions and high-profile Christian speakers, while various smaller rooms round the side were for workshops and seminars on a variety of subjects but all connected with music-making in church. I soon met up with the rest of the deputation from St Basil's, and at four thirty exactly we began. Our hard work on Wednesday had certainly paid off, and our so-called regional contribution went well, the large audience applauding enthusiastically after each item.

We finished at ten past five and with some time to kill before the praise party, I decided to see what the workshops had to offer. Amazingly enough, there was a workshop on preparing and printing choir music by PC. It was an utterly absorbing hour and a quarter, and I was quite sorry when the leader looked at his watch and said that we ought to be taking our places for the praise party.

The next half hour was every bit as ghastly as I had feared; a massive crowd was now crushed into the main hall, and to the accompaniment of deafening amplified electric guitars and keyboard on the podium at the front, we sang a succession of choruses all of which appeared to be unannounced with no music or words to help us. In between each one there was a host of inaudible exchanges between various individuals on the podium, as well as little guffaws of laughter indicative of some private joke the significance of which was denied to lesser mortals. Somewhat naughtily, I thought if this was a party of praise to God, I'd hate to think what these people do to him when he upsets them.

Finally, at seven, a cacophonous clash of guitar, cymbal and synthesiser was followed by a rapturous burst of applause, and then....silence. It was over! I was so overcome with relief that I looked round to the young girl on my right and was about to engage in some pleasant farewell banter with her when the music suddenly started again and to another wave of applause, a huge overhead projector screen was switched on above the band with the words WELCOME TO THE COME AND PRAISE PARTY!!!! "What's going on, do you think?" I asked the girl. She replied "That was just the warm-up for the band. This is it now."

Decided that 'it' could happen without me, and left the hall, reminding myself that I had taken part in the regional contribution which was what really mattered, and the crowd of ecstatic worshippers was so great that nobody was now likely to miss me.

Then the fun really began. On arrival back at my car, the rain now almost tropical in its ferocity, I found a whole line of cars had parked up parallel with mine and it was impossible for me to get out. For a ghastly moment I had visions of sitting in my car for possibly several hours with nothing to entertain me besides the sleeve notes for my *Crucifixion* CD and an old street atlas of the principal towns of Buckinghamshire. A few moments' reconnaissance, however, convinced me that I could actually get round the blockage by driving my car across the green and on to a metalled slip road just fifty yards away. Confidently I started the car, drove on to the green....and promptly came to a grinding halt. On exiting from the car, I saw all too clearly what had happened. The green, now soaked by days and weeks of incessant rain, had taken on the texture of a mangrove swamp in the monsoon season and was as pleasant to walk on as a layer of slime-coated porridge. The wheels of my car simply could not force their way over it. Hard revving of my engine only served to dig the wheels deeper into the abyss, and plunge my heart deeper into the soles of my Hush Puppies.

Fortunately I had my mobile so I was able to telephone the AA, but news from the other end of the line only served to deepen the general gloom. Because of the number of cars that had succumbed to floodwater in other parts of the capital, there would be a delay of two hours before a unit could reach me.

I sat numbly in my car for a while, consoling myself with the thought that at least the praise party was still likely to be in full swing long after my vehicle had been hauled from the mire. The whole thing might almost have formed the basis for a psalm: "They dragged me into the dreadful dark pit of mud; but the ranks of the goodly people brought me out again and verily I rejoiced at it." I was beginning to wonder how I might perhaps work it into the entertainment slot at the next choir party when I heard voices and saw coming towards me a whole host of people who were instantly recognisable as having been at the convention. Within minutes all the cars around mine had gone. The last to leave was a man who I recognised as having been in my PC workshop and who claimed to have set up his very own website for Christians wanting to be trendy – "www sensible shoes aren't us.com" I think he'd called it. I couldn't resist approaching him and asking him what had happened. "Oh, we finished on time," he said. "We had to be out by quarter to eight. The local drama group were having the hall after us for their dress rehearsal for *The Devil's Disciple*." He pointed to my car and said "This isn't half a rough area, you know. Cars abandoned everywhere. I don't think that old rust-bucket will fight its way out of there in a hurry." Whereupon he got into his car and drove off. For a trendy Christian night out, no doubt.

By the time the AA man finally arrived, at twenty minutes to ten, I had gone through enough emotions to provide material for a whole new book of psalms – and that without recourse to meting out the valley of Succoth or being closed in by fat bulls of Basan. Fortunately their sturdy breakdown truck succeeded in dislodging my own vehicle, and by ten thirty I was at last on my way, at the cost not only of three completely wasted hours but a fiver to put my car through the wash and half that again for a packet of crisps and a bar of chocolate to sustain me for the two-and-a-half-hour drive home.

But at least I now consider myself a leading authority on the tonal infrastructure of Stainer's *Crucifixion*. And an assuredly unparalleled expert on the High Wycombe ring-road system in the late seventies.

Sunday 17th March – *FIFTH SUNDAY IN LENT*

I somehow dragged myself to church this morning after just five hours' sleep last night. A small congregation, a weak choir – which I noticed contained none of yesterday's attenders apart from myself – and Tripplehorn in a subdued mood. He didn't seem to flinch at all when Matthew started smirking on realising that the psalm chant was by one William Crotch and the anthem, *O Sacrum Convivium*, by a composer who was named Croce but also pronounced Crotch.

I came away with a strange feeling of anticlimax. I never thought I'd hear myself say it, but I had quite enjoyed our choir slot yesterday, with crowds of enthusiastic and committed singers, and a vociferous receptive congregation. It's hard to say the same for the attenders of St Basil's. To hear some of the second sops you wonder why they bother to kick off their bedsocks of a Sunday morning. As for the congregation, I suppose everything is relative. Maybe I'm just unfortunate enough to belong to a church whose members are regarded as vociferous if they sing the words of at least one of the hymns– hymns, that is, of which they know the tune and are able to find in their hymn book before the last verse –and perceived as receptive if they haven't dropped dead in the middle of the sermon.

An extra practice this afternoon to cover the Holy Week music including the *Crucifixion* on Palm Sunday, for which I am to sing the tenor solo. I was pleased with my rendition and I got some nice compliments. The sunrise service on Easter Sunday is going to be an extraordinary affair – the Holy Saturday liturgies in church at 5.30am and then processing to the top of Castle Hill to welcome in the Easter morn. "So pray for fine weather, for God's sake," said Tripplehorn. Craig Dumbleton told me the last time he'd taken part in a sunrise service on Castle Hill it had been a disaster. "It rained, then, did it?" I asked him. "Wish it had," he replied. "No, the gates were locked and we ended up celebrating the resurrection glory in front of the Bradford and Bingley."

The music for Good Friday was predictably fairly heavy-going. Zoe Sparkes turned to her mum and asked her "If Jesus has risen why do we still have to sing such sad music on Good Friday?" As always, poor Alison was completely stumped for an answer. If Zoe's brother's the next Ben Elton, she's the next Jeremy Paxman.

Friday 22nd March

I knew it was a fatal mistake to plan to meet a couple of friends this weekend for Sunday lunch and an afternoon walk. Having re-assured us over a period of several weeks that he didn't want to tire us out by rehearsing the Stainer on Sunday afternoon, Tripplehorn told us at the start of tonight's rehearsal that he would need us on Sunday afternoon after all.

Later in the practice he seemed to have a change of heart, for having not looked at the Stainer at all he suddenly, with five minutes' official rehearsing time to go, said "Right. Let's run the Stainer."

Whether or not it was relief that he appeared to be trying to avoid the Sunday practice I don't know, but we threw ourselves into it and over the next hour and ten minutes gave a robust and at times passionate performance. At one point I could almost feel myself there, among the baying crowds in the sweltering heat of the Jerusalem noonday, or looking up at that tortured, haggard face of an innocent man who gave his life for the redemption of mankind.

"Well, that was interesting," Tripplehorn said when we reached the end. "I still prefer Stainer's *Crucifixion*, myself. Two o'clock here, Sunday. And count yourself lucky if you're out again by five."

Now I know how cargo ship stowaways must feel when they emerge from the hold hoping to be inhaling the sweet perfumes of Zanzibar or the fragrant incense of Arabia and find themselves on the Woolwich free ferry.

Sunday 24th March – *PALM SUNDAY*

An early start to the service today, with the procession from the Sheepmarket Car Park to the church. In previous years, apparently, we have simply sung the hymn *All Glory Laud and Honour* whilst processing, but this year it was decided to sing the words to a different tune in the form of a round, to create a more dynamic effect. Choir members were asked to round up members of the congregation into groups, each group coming in at different times to create the round. What perhaps none of us bargained for was that Sheepmarket Street, the quickest way from the car park to the church, was being closed all day for essential gas main repairs, and our route had to take us via Sheep Lane, Southlands Terrace, Alexandra Road, Station Approach, Marshalsea Crescent and Lady Ponsonby's Passage. By the time we'd finally entered the church, not only had the round disintegrated into fragments of feeble chants that would have sounded lack-lustre even by comparison with the supporters of a Doctor Martens Football League away side losing 4-0 at halftime, but we still faced five hymns, the 32-verse psalm 22, the plainchant declamation of the Passion according to St Matthew, and a six-page anthem.

By a supreme effort we managed to convey the mixed message of Palm Sunday – the joyful acclamation of Jesus on his entry to Jerusalem and then, so swiftly afterwards, the brutal demands for his life, with a corresponding change of musical mood from bright and exuberant to melancholic and penitential. But at the end of it all I felt shattered, told Tripplehorn that I really needed to rest my voice during the afternoon and asked him if I could be excused the rehearsal. "I really do need you to be there," he said. "I shall want you to help the tenors out in the chorus bits. If it's your voice you're worried about, come back and have lunch with me. I've got just the thing for knackered voices."

Having put my friends off yesterday, I was free for lunch so accepted his invitation. Lesley Markwick and her boyfriend Barry were there, as was Craig Dumbleton. While we were waiting for the soup and baguettes to heat up, Tripplehorn played us a recording of the previous year's performance of the Stainer. The tenor soloist was all over the shop. I looked at the accompanying programme which pronounced the soloist to be one Charles Ollerenshaw. "Awful man," Tripplehorn commented. "Yes," I said. "It sounds as though he'd had a few before you recorded this. He's really got no idea, has he?" "Actually," said Craig Dumbleton, "he was taken ill just before that recording and it's not him singing." "Oh," I said, "who is it, then?" "Me," said Craig Dumbleton.

I was so thrown by his response that I was unable to think straight after that, and forgot to go home to fetch my copy of the score of the *Crucifixion*. Fortunately when I arrived in the vestry I saw a spare unclaimed copy lying on the window-sill, and was able to use that. The rehearsal was a shambles, and we finished with barely an hour to go before the performance was due to begin. By the time I had organised the teas and cakes – we'd been warned there might be insufficient time to get home in between – it was almost 6.30 when we were due to go back in and start the performance.

It was then that the trouble began. Tripplehorn called us together and said "I understand that we were a copy short this afternoon. One of you children has obviously lost your copy, am I right?" Somewhat sheepishly, Matthew Sparkes admitted that he had left his copy lying around after last Friday's practice. Tripplehorn went ballistic. "How the heck do you think you can sing properly without your own copy?" he demanded. "I'll tell you this. Another lost copy – and this goes for any of you – and I shan't be responsible for the consequences." Suddenly, to my horror, I realised that the copy I'd been using this afternoon must be Matthew's – suspicions which were instantly confirmed when I saw that the note on the second page "Running time – 70 minutes" had been changed in pencil to "70 years." I lost no time in returning my copy to Matthew, but by now there were barely five minutes to go before the start, and with Tripplehorn's words ringing in my ear, I was in no position to own up that I was now copy-less. Desperately, I rifled through the music cupboard and to my amazement, almost at once found a copy of the *Crucifixion*. Mightily relieved, I processed in with the choir, took my place at the front – the soloists' prerogative – and opened my copy, ready for my opening recitative. The introductory organ music seemed to bear little relation to what I had in front of me and a hideous thought crossed my mind. My worst fears were confirmed when I glanced at the title page and saw, to my horror, that this was not the *Crucifixion* by Stainer, but the *Crucifixion* by Edward Higginbottom, with words by Dr Raymond Proudfoot-Jones. Panic. I drew upon the deepest recesses of my memory and blurted out the opening recitative "And they came to a place." Except I couldn't for the life of me remember the name of the place and rewrote the entire first episode of the

Passion story by informing my listeners that the place of Jesus' betrayal was Gennesaret.

Mercifully, Joan Trumpington saw that something was amiss and hurried across to me with a copy of Stainer's version, but by now my confidence had evaporated and my performance was, if anything, less convincing than that of Craig Dumbleton last year. To add insult to injury, Henry Peasgood came up to me afterwards and said "Was that Stainer or Higginbottom who was crucifying Jesus tonight, then?" I'd have felt more comfortable languishing in Lady Ponsonby's Passage.

Thursday 28th March – *MAUNDY THURSDAY*

I confided in Rachel that I was getting seriously cold feet about the liturgical marathon in the early hours of Easter Sunday morning. "Oh, you've got to be there," she replied. I was quite touched by her obvious admiration for my contribution to our musical devotion. Until she went on "If I'm going to get the giggles, I shall at least want someone to share the joke." I think there was a compliment there somewhere.

Tripplehorn seemed in a better mood tonight, rubbing his hands and saying "Looking forward to the stripping later on, then?" to the nauseating delight of Lesley Markwick. He was of course referring to the stripping of the altar following tonight's sung eucharist. A surprisingly good congregation and a big choir which included Jane for the first time for weeks. She gave me a big hug and a kiss on both cheeks. Rachel would then have to go and spoil it by saying "Oh, Jane, you can't do that, he's spoken for now. What would poor Margaret say?" To which Jane responded "So you're with Margaret now. I hope you'll be very happy together" – before walking smartly off to try and locate a folder of music. I made a mental note to cross Rachel off my Easter egg list.

A beautiful service, the ending of which was perfectly choreographed: as we sang Allegri's *Miserere*, the priest and the altar party slowly removed the altar decorations and dimmed the lights to leave a bare table in semi-gloom, a reminder that we were moving from the commemoration of Jesus' first entreaty to his disciples to remember him through bread and wine, to the terrifying darkness of death and the seeming triumph of the powers of evil through the tyranny of sin. I felt almost tearful as we declaimed those immortal lines from Psalm 51 – "Wash me throughly from my wickedness, and cleanse me from my sin." One by one the large congregation made their solemn exit from the church, as directed, without noise or ceremony, and finally, having reached the last verse, we too walked penitentially and gravely into the vestry. The atmosphere was hushed, reverential and in its

way quite emotional. But broken as soon as we arrived in the vestry by Irving Cattermole who threw on the lights and shouted "Anyone remember to tape *The Bill*?"
Needless to say, he was never on my Easter egg list to begin with.

Friday 29th March – *GOOD FRIDAY*

A welcome lie-in was followed by breakfast with the special Easter edition of *Basil's Bits*, our monthly church newsletter. On page 3, below an advertisement for a performance of Bach's *St John Passion* half an hour's drive away, was a letter from our vicar deploring the commercialisation of Good Friday and inviting shops and businesses to think twice before opening their doors on this holiest of days when our minds should be turned towards self-denial and self-examination.

We arrived promptly at one for our rehearsal for this afternoon's service. The assistant priest, for whose benefit the rehearsal was being called as he had a number of sung parts to do, was nowhere to be seen. Eventually he hurried through the door, breathless, at ten past. "I'm so sorry," he said, "You wouldn't believe the queues in Asda."

Before the service, Cora Willoughby-Smith announced that as usual she would be toasting hot cross buns at 5.00pm with a video showing of the crucifixion scene from Zeffirelli's *Jesus Of Nazareth*. I was quite tempted, as I find that film quite incredibly moving, but as I was robing Lesley whispered to me "Be warned. She'll expect you all to stay on and listen to her selection of solos from grand opera." Enough said.

The service was an anticlimax after last night. The congregation was reasonable enough, but the music was uniformly gloomy and our plainchant Passion, so perfectly in tune on Palm Sunday, slipped at least a tone today. I tried hard to re-enact in my mind's eye the sheer physical agony of Jesus – the brutal flogging, the crown of sharp thorns pressing relentlessly into his head, the nails being driven violently through the hands that had stretched out to bless and embrace mankind. I wondered if mere words could ever do justice to the enormity of what happened on the first Good Friday. I felt strangely down on arrival home. Then I remembered the *St John Passion* tonight. I thought if the immortal music of Bach failed to attune my mind to the true significance of this day, nothing could, and I decided to go. On impulse, I rang Jane and asked her to come with me. She readily agreed and I arranged to pick her up at six thirty.

When we met I was somewhat taken aback to see her in a very revealing low cut top and denim hot pants, which I thought seemed more appropriate to a rave than a serious sacred concert. I was even more puzzled, as we drove

there, by her statement first of all that "I didn't think this would be quite your sort of thing" and then that "I've heard fab reviews about this gig" but did not query it further. It was only when we stopped outside St Mary's Church and she asked "Are you sure this is where he's performing?" that I got the feeling that she was not after all anticipating an evening in the company of Johann Sebastian Bach. My suspicions were confirmed when as we walked down the church path, she said "I think I misunderstood you. I thought we were going to see Jon Masson. In concert with the Electric Squeals. I didn't think they were in this area till June."

To give her her due, she did accept it was probably her mistake and that she would be quite happy to listen to the *St John Passion* with me. But it took her some while to make up her mind, and consequently we had only a minute or two to spare before the performance began. By now the church was virtually full, and we found ourselves stuck right behind a pillar, making it quite impossible for us to see anything. As if that was not enough, Jane's hot pants were so short that there was no protection for the resultant acres of bare flesh against the ice-cold rock-hard pews.

Thankfully we were told there was to be an interval, hence an opportunity to disappear, after forty-five minutes, but it was the longest three quarters of an hour of my life. Cora was quite surprised to see us back at her house, especially as we'd missed the hot cross buns and the video. "Never mind," she said, "You're just in time to see Arthur Ramsbottom's film of the choir outing to Weymouth three years ago." This was more than even Jane could stand, and she announced she was feeling a bit tired and could do with an early night. Various others promptly made their excuses, leaving just Cora, Arthur and myself to watch nearly two hours of third-rate filming with only rare shots of choir members and lengthy studies either of Arthur's sister or a stretch of sand which could have been Bermuda or Bognor.

As an exercise in self-denial and self-examination it could hardly have been improved upon. Perhaps I ought to go one better next year and book up to see Jon Masson and the Electric Squeals. With Cora Willoughby-Smith's dying lament of *Aida* as the warm-up act.

Sunday 31st March – *EASTER DAY*

Apart from the fact that there were precisely six people in the congregation, the illumination for the opening chants was so sparse that it was impossible to see what we were supposed to be singing, the Easter fire failed to light, I came in with two chants I was cantoring three prayers too early, the Sparkes overslept and arrived an hour late, the vicar spoke rather than intoned a gospel acclamation we had practised every Friday evening for the past six weeks, the homily from today's guest preacher Douglas Perfrement was so long that at least three choir members were seen to be trying to make up for being roused from their beds at four thirty in the morning, Lesley Markwick got the giggles during the plainchant Litany of the Saints when requesting the assistance of one St Athanasius, the note given for the Easter Anthems was at least two tones too high, and once again the keeper of Castle Hill had evidently decided a contingent of worshippers from the town's parish church represented too great a threat to the preservation of the ancient fortification thus forcing us to proclaim the glorious Easter message to what was now the Happy House Tandoori, our early morning act of worship was a roaring success.

Thankfully the main Easter morning service was everything one could have hoped for: a packed congregation, the church beautifully decorated, the address inspiring and uplifting, and the music superb. After the farce that our earlier act of worship had been, it was truly wonderful to take our places in St James' Chapel for our rendition of Charles Wood's *This Joyful Eastertide*, a glorious introit to this feast of Resurrection joy, and then to process to our stalls past the crowds of people, who were in some cases spilling into the aisles. Although we have as a choir been told off in the past for acknowledging members of the congregation during a procession, I couldn't help ignoring that instruction today, especially as I'd not seen some of them for months. We enjoyed six rousing hymns, Psalm 98 and Henry Ley's *The Strife Is O'er,* one of my favourite anthems. In the sermon the vicar had a go at those whose religion is not C of E but C and E – i.e. Christmas and Easter – and suggested that St Basil's might have something to offer them at other times. What those times were remained unspecified, but after today I shouldn't suppose they'll include half past five on a Sunday morning after the clocks have gone forward.

I had a nice afternoon lined up: a well-earned drink, forty winks and then a drive to the village of Pratton All Saints, where the tea-room had just won Best Tea Place In The South award, before popping round to see John, Alex and the twins with an Easter egg in the early evening. Just as I was leaving, Brian and Rachel buttonholed me and planted a huge bag of mini-eggs into my hand, then asked me if I would like to join them for Easter Sunday lunch. "As a thank you for coming this morning," Rachel said.

A quite delicious roast lamb was followed by a scrummy banoffi pie, all liberally washed down with some vintage Burgundy which Brian had brought back from Paris a fortnight ago. The house was warm and I was beginning to feel the effects of the early start this morning. The result was that when we finished eating at three thirty, I crashed out on the luxuriously deep settee and was soon sound asleep, being only awoken at four fifty by Rachel offering me a cup of tea and rich fruit cake. "Arthur Ramsbottom will be here in a minute," she said. "He lost his wife on Easter Sunday six years ago and he gets very lonely at this time of year." Despite the fact that I fancied a good long walk to clear my head, I felt morally obliged to remain, and having dropped a few spiritual brownie points by my well-oiled lunchtime re-enactment of some of the more absurd aspects of this morning's fiasco, was determined to retrieve them now. Still, despite Rachel's concern for his well-being, I felt there was no need for her to respond quite so positively to his suggestion that we all view his film of the choir outing to Weymouth – the very same film I'd seen just two days before. The only relief came in the form of Tripplehorn, who somehow knew where I was, and who popped in to give me some Herbert Bumfrey compositions for reprinting on the computer. What he conveniently omitted to tell me, and I did not find out till after he'd gone, was that the bundle consisted of six or seven anthems, some of them a good ten pages long. Also, according to the scrawled note which accompanied them, he wanted them all done by Friday night's practice so we could look at them in advance of the Bumfrey workshop day.

Then it was back to the film.

By the time it had finished, I think I knew every grain of sand on that beach and every detail of Arthur's sister Daisy that day. From the number of chips she consumed at lunchtime to the number of times she complained to the camera about the verruca on her left foot.

APRIL

Easter Monday 1st April

The telephone rang at half past eight. "This is Joan Trumpington," I was told. She sounded most peculiar. "I'm sorry to disturb you so early on Easter Monday, but the choir have been asked at very short notice to feature in an *EastEnders* special they're recording in Overbush. A couple of the characters are getting married and having a country church wedding, and they want a choir. There's a big fee and you'll get the chance to meet all the big names." Being a huge fan of *EastEnders*, I was overjoyed. "When do they want us?" I asked. "Nine thirty this morning," was the reply. "And if I were you....." Suddenly the speaker was interrupted by the unmistakeable voice of Alison in the choir. "What do you think you're doing, child!" she screeched. A moment later the line went dead.

I suppose Matthew's April foolery did have its funny side. It rather took me back to my schooldays and the ingenious seasonal japes of my classmate Ackroyd Minor. His teachers used to pray that April 1st fell in the school holidays. I redressed the balance by leaving a message on Tripplehorn's answering machine pretending to be the manager of a cable TV company wanting to give blanket coverage to the workshop day, with interviews and musical excerpts.

I had a free evening so decided to get working on the Bumfrey whilst enjoying the live football that was on TV tonight. Accordingly, I unplugged my printer and put on my portable telly. By ten forty I had almost done the whole wretched assignment and watched an excellent game of football. Then the phone rang. It was Tripplehorn. "You'll never believe this," he cried excitedly, "but we're going to have live TV coverage of our Herbert Bumfrey workshop day!" He sounded so enthusiastic that I decided I couldn't own up – until he went on "I'm going to tell the local press all about it and if people think they're going to be on TV, they'll come in their droves." It was at this point that I realised I would have to come clean, and did so.

His tone not surprisingly changed considerably. "Well," he snapped, "That's just about put the seal on my night. My television on the blink, and now this."

I felt duty bound, under the circumstances, to offer to bring my portable round for him at once. As soon as I'd hung up, I switched the telly off, pulled out the plug – and saw my computer screen die and five hours' work instantly consigned to oblivion.

If this was divine punishment for my April foolery, it seems excessively harsh. I don't recall Ackroyd Minor getting any more than half an hour's detention for shoving boiled rice down Mr Pauncefoot's exhaust pipe.

Friday 5th April

We got through our music for Sunday in record time, as Tripplehorn wanted to devote most of the practice to preparations for the workshop day. Last night I had managed to prepare and print three pieces, having picked up some time-saving tips from Tony Smart, and reeled off three more before coming out tonight. I have to say that with the illustrations on each page, the end product was extremely pleasing. We spent some time this evening looking at two of the anthems, based on parts of Psalms 57 and 69, *They Have Digged A Pit Before Me and I Stick Fast In The Deep Mire.* I thought Rachel was quite brave to inquire openly if Bumfrey was a composer or a drainage engineer.

The last half-hour, although it seemed twice as long, was devoted to practical arrangements for the day. We begin with coffee at 9.30, then sing through until 1 with another coffee break at 11. We resume at two, and after another break at four will sing evensong at 4.30, consisting of three hymns with music by Herbert Bumfrey, the psalms appointed for the thirteenth evening with chants by Herbert Bumfrey, the Magnificat and Nunc Dimittis to the Sixth Service setting in A flat by Herbert Bumfrey, Versicles and Responses by Herbert Bumfrey, and the anthem *My Soul Is Among Lions* by…………Herbert Bumfrey. So he's not a drainage engineer. He works in a zoo.

We then discussed catering. Everyone was asked to contribute a plate of something. Cora Willoughby-Smith offered her speciality Pork In Cider With Prune Stuffing. Queenie Haverthwaite will prepare her much-loved Cream of Artichoke and Celery Broth with apple-smoked cheese bread. And Craig Dumbleton said he'd bring a packet of six individual fruit tarts from the Co-op.

As usual, I'm lumbered with the coffee and tea.

It was only right at the end of the evening that there was discussion on the numbers. Tripplehorn was supremely confident that at least half the population within a two hundred mile radius knew that it was going on, several people had told him that they *hoped to* be there, several more had indicated that they *should be* there, an even greater number had told him that they *would like to* be there, but he seemed curiously vague about the number of people who actually *would* be there. In answer to that very question, he replied "Well, you all will be, of course. Oh, and I tell you what. That girl who runs the Oxfam shop in Hill Parade – her boyfriend's father's sister's best friend – she's very excited about it."

Perhaps it might be a little premature for me to book an appointment with the manager of Tesco to negotiate a discounted price for bulk purchases of Nescafe and PG Tips.

Sunday 7th April – *FIRST SUNDAY AFTER EASTER*

As might have been expected, church this morning was a big anticlimax after last Sunday. An exceedingly feeble congregation, half the choir seemed to be away, and the vicar was taking a well-earned holiday. The substitute correctly announced our anthem as *Cantate Domino* by Pitoni but pronounced Cantate as though it were Cantait, and then told the congregation that the choir would end the service by singing John Rutter's *Garlic Blessing*. Perhaps we should be grateful we weren't singing *Panis Angelicus*.

Tuesday 9th April

I knew it was a mistake giving Tripplehorn my e-mail address at work. When I got back from quite a long and difficult meeting there was an e-mail from him saying he was desperate for more definite yesses for Saturday and was asking every choir member to ring three people and personally invite them to the Herbert Bumfrey workshop day. The fact that they, like we, will be asked to contribute £10 towards the expenses of the day and the church roof fund is something we can apparently conveniently forget to remind them.

During a window between the news and *EastEnders*, I picked three former singing friends at random from my address book. The first was Emily Harding, on whom I'd had a massive crush in the glee club and who was living not far from where I am now. I rang the number only to find she'd left that address some five years ago and was now thought to be breeding pot-bellied pigs on the Isle of Lewis.

I had more luck in making contact with the second, another glee club friend who'd gravitated to this area a couple of years back and who I knew to be an outstandingly talented musician. He said he'd been asked to play second violin on Saturday in Mahler's *Resurrection Symphony* at the Royal Albert Hall. "But I'd love to join you," he went on, "if by any chance all two thousand ticket holders cry off and we have to cancel." He always was a caustic clever-dick.

Finally I tried Gerald Goff, an old school friend. Almost as soon as our conversation began I regretted having bothered him, for with no prompting whatsoever on my part, he launched into an unutterably tedious diatribe on the internal politics of the electronics department of the technical college at which he is a senior lecturer, followed up with an even less inspiring lecture on the parlous state of our internal waterways. To my horror, he then announced there was nothing he'd like more than to spend a pleasant Saturday singing the works of an undiscovered British composer and would I mind collecting him from the station at nine o'clock.

So there it is then. A precious Saturday alternating between Herbert Bumfrey's deep mire, and Gerard Goff holding forth upon the sewage content of the Manchester Ship Canal.

Saturday 13th April

To go into the full horrors of the Herbert Bumfrey workshop day would occupy more pages of this diary than I can reasonably spare, so I will simply confine myself to a number of suggestions to future readers of the diary should they in future be imbecilic enough to organise something similar either for Herbert Bumfrey or any other, equally deservedly unknown, composer of English church music.

ONE – ensure that there are enough copies to share one between two rather than one between three and a half. Nobody can be expected to have brought their own, for the simple reason that nobody in their right mind would have purchased their own in the first place.

TWO – just because a large outspoken lady in the front row happily announces that she is so entranced by the majesty of the music that she is quite happy to sing right through the entire morning without a tea and biscuit break, it should not be assumed that her views are shared by everyone else, particularly those who needlessly queued up in the mini-mart for twenty minutes to pay for a packet of chocolate digestives.

THREE – don't automatically believe that because the local press photographer has three months beforehand vaguely promised to attend at five thirty to take a group photo following the conclusion of the workshop, it is worth hanging around until twenty past six in the hope that he will actually turn up.

FOUR – if you as choirmaster are going to record one of the pieces of this unknown composer for posterity, and spend half an hour going through the piece some twelve times to perfect it for the microphone, then obtain a faultless performance for the purpose, remember to switch the RECORD button on the cassette player before you do it.

FIVE – if you as choirmaster are disappointed that the tenor line is incapable, after two attempts at a piece, of reproducing the exact dynamic

59

and artistic intentions of the composer, you should, if you ever wish to work with any of the singers on similar projects again, resist the temptation to compel each singer to give a solo rendition of the tenor line of the piece in question and then liken each individual effort to anything from a rusty Reliant Robin on a cold morning to a Moulinex mixer grinding a bagful of peppermint humbugs.

SIX – It should not be taken for granted that choir members, having spent the entire morning singing the works of an inferior composer, should want to spend a good thirty per cent of their precious lunch break being provided with an exhaustive biography of him, detailing everything from his hospitality towards his neighbourhood's stray cat population to his penchant for cooked fish first thing in the morning.

SEVEN – If the preces and responses involve intonations by the precentor that are of unusual difficulty, it is a good idea to warn him in advance rather than slap them on his lectern two minutes before the start of the service and expect him to make anything other than a total mockery of them.

EIGHT – If you organise a service to represent the culmination of the day's toils and wish for a congregation consisting of more than three elderly ladies seated almost as far away from the choir as it is possible to get, it is advisable to avoid holding it at the same time as the Mayor's civic parade through the streets, the major art exhibition and collector's fayre at the Town Hall, and the annual Fairyglen Country Park pond duck race.

NINE – The fact that outside participants in the event describe the day as "different," "novel," "adventurous" and "interesting" should not be automatically construed as meaning they have found it the slightest bit enjoyable or fulfilling, and should certainly not be interpreted as an invitation to repeat it in a year's time in the context of a full week's residential course. Doubtless with deep-fried haddock for breakfast.

Sunday 14th April – *SECOND SUNDAY AFTER EASTER*

Nice to be singing decent music again at church this morning. Even Wood's *O Thou The Central Orb*, which I think is hugely over-rated, seemed to assume an almost celestial beauty. The vicar announced that yesterday's efforts had raised the grand total of £168 for the church roof. I think an equivalent sum could have been raised with less physical, emotional and mental effort by organising a house-to-house collection round the suburbs of Beirut. Ironically, the PCC are now having to dig into their pockets not only for the roof but for the outside vestry door that was vandalised last night and is consequently unusable. We're having to enter into the church through the main door for the next week and a half at least.

Still, the relief of having got yesterday behind us was quite palpable both before and after the service. Over coffee, I got talking to a young couple I'd never seen in church before. It turned out they'd had their banns read in church this morning. They remarked on what a nice service it had been, and how they were really keen for our choir to sing for them at their wedding in a few weeks. One of today's sidesmen, whose name I keep forgetting, was hovering nearby, and being in a frivolous mood, I said to him "Another couple who say they loved the service but who we won't see for dust once they've sped off in their wedding limousine. Bit of a cheek, don't you think?" "Perhaps not," he replied, "considering they're going to be spending their first year of married life doing Christian mission work among some of the poorest people in South America." I said I was surprised the vicar hadn't mentioned this when reading the banns. "Oh, well, my son and future daughter-in-law aren't ones for blowing their own trumpet," he replied.

I think in future I'll stick to chatting to Millicent Treadwell about her ingrowing toenails.

Wednesday 17th April

Today's post brought a letter from Tripplehorn thanking us for last Saturday and in particular for bringing to life the works of an unsung genius. Genius hardly, but unsung in every sense and with every justification.

The letter went on to set out the proposed programme for the concert which is to take place on the 18th of next month. A Bumfrey-free zone, thank goodness. It is a splendid selection of music – Brahms, Stainer, Mendelssohn, Parry, Purcell, Rutter, and much more. The bad news is that we are all expected to flog at least ten tickets each, and we are urged to consider whom we might approach. Gerald Goff was the first and most obvious name that came to mind, but I cannot immediately think of any member of the congregation who deserves, still less needs, to have their fill of inspirational musical offerings to the Lord supplemented, as my singing had been on the Bumfrey day, with woebegone monologues on the excessive dredging of marine aggregates from the Humber Estuary or the unacceptable levels of undergrowth on the banks of the Shepperton Loops.

Friday 19th April

Much of the early evening spent on the phone trying to sell my quota of tickets. I never knew that so much else happened in town on Saturday nights in mid-May: bridge evenings, school reunions, theatre workshops, simultaneous chess exhibitions by a Russian grand master, and, the undoubted highlight of the town's social calendar, the Upper South

Newdigate Street Infants' School parent-teacher association wine and cheese and bowling evening. Finally, I did manage to extract an expression of interest out of Patricia Glenwood, one of the church flower arrangers. She said she was really looking forward to attending and spoke in positively gushing terms about the choir, their loyalty and enthusiasm, and their enhancement of the life of the church, and that she would be delighted to support any venture they may be pleased to undertake. I asked her if she'd like a ticket and she said "You're the twelfth person who's asked me that this evening."

The concert is going to be on the theme of "Journey Through Life." We spent most of this evening's practice, at which I was the only tenor, looking at Rutter's delightful setting of *All Things Bright And Beautiful*, Purcell's *Thou Knowest Lord* and Parry's *I Was Glad*. During a well-earned pause for breath after running the Parry it was announced that Ken Foulkes, whom we've not seen since Palm Sunday, is still very frail following major heart surgery during Holy Week, and as it was his birthday today it had been arranged with his wife that we'd go and serenade him at home. It was a mite surprising, having regard to his infirmity, that he should be so keen to hear us sing the Purcell, with the words "suffer us not at our last hour for any pains of death to fall from thee." Tripplehorn was particularly scathing about our diction, telling us it sounded "less like a desperate prayer for mercy and deliverance than a list of types of tinned dogfood."

At last, after several encores, we got it to an acceptable standard and trooped round to see Ken himself. Jane was there tonight, extremely friendly towards me, and we even shared a joke about the events of Good Friday evening. As we made our way to Ken's house I suggested that the two of us should do a duet in the concert, and to my delight she said she'd love to. Perhaps inspired by her friendliness and willingness to sing with me, I did an excellent job of the tenor line in the Purcell, and the overall effect was really very moving. Matthew, despite his delinquent tendencies, has a lovely treble voice, and in the absence of the older ladies, who decided they'd had enough by nine o'clock, we actually sounded almost professional. Ken sat there, looking tired but obviously very thankful. It certainly made our hard labours of earlier this evening worthwhile. At the end, after he had applauded us, Tripplehorn said "There we are. Not up to Kings College standard perhaps, but still." "To be honest," Ken replied, "it's just nice to see some friendly faces. For all I cared, you could have come and sung me the latest advert for Pedigree Chum." It's good to know that the eleven runthroughs were worthwhile.

Sunday 21ˢᵗ April – *THIRD SUNDAY AFTER EASTER*

Arrived at church to find quite a few more cars parked outside than usual. "Baptism," Brian Ellis explained. "Though an FIC job by all accounts." In response to my blank look, he went on "Short for Fags In Churchyard. People who never normally darken church doors and are terrified of the prospect of a whole hour without lighting up." His prophecy proved to be uncannily accurate, for the air was thick with cigarette fumes and the ground littered with dog ends as we made our way up to the front door. I went into church and was immediately buttonholed by Molly Plunkett, the duty sidesman, who gave me a broad smile, shook my hand and said to me "Welcome to our church. Here's a hymn book and a pew sheet and if you like there are some brief historical notes about our beautiful building just to the left there as well as a welcome leaflet with details of our services and special events. I take it you're one of the baptism party?" Yet it was barely 36 hours ago that I'd been on the phone to her trying to sell her a ticket for the choir concert. So much for my impact on music-making at St Basil's.

We were going to do Wesley's *Lead Me Lord* as the anthem, but Tripplehorn decided to change it at the last minute to Rutter's *All Things Bright And Beautiful*. He explained "Not only did we do it on Friday and it's a useful extra rehearsal for the concert but some of the punters may actually recognise the words. From the last time they were in church, twenty years ago."

During the sermon I leafed through the hymn book to find the offertory hymn, which I noticed was also *All Things Bright And Beautiful*. When the time came to sing the hymn, Tripplehorn played over not the familiar tune but the introductory organ music for the Rutter anthem, which we weren't due to sing until communion. To make matters worse, while some of us had the presence of mind to locate the anthem straight away, others just stood there blankly, and to put the icing on the cake, a number of members of the congregation started joining in, some with Rutter's music, some with the hymn tune, and some with a string of notes which could have been the final chorus of *Cosi Fan Tutte* or Humpty Dumpty Sat On a Wall.

I think after that lot I could have used a fag myself.

Monday 22ⁿᵈ April

Got a call from Godfrey Trimble, the PCC secretary, at a quarter to ten tonight advising me that Hazel Ledworthy no longer wishes to stand as choir representative on the PCC and would I be interested in being nominated for the post at the annual church meeting that takes place on Wednesday week. "It's a tremendous honour," he told me. "You'd be helping to make decisions that shape the future of our church life and providing a valuable perspective as a comparative newcomer with fresh ideas while making a significant contribution to the choral aspect of our liturgical tradition."

I told him I'd think about it. I certainly feel extremely honoured and flattered to have been asked, and pleased that I have evidently convinced our church hierarchy that I can play a worthwhile part in enhancing our worship and at the same time help to consolidate God's Kingdom within our community.

Almost immediately I'd hung up, Rachel rang to invite me to tea tomorrow night. "I'd have rung you sooner, but that wretched Gilbert Tremble was bending my ear for half an hour about my joining the PCC," she said. "When he asked me I knew he was really scraping the barrel."

Wednesday 24th April

Another letter from West Shires, advising me that as a result of my failure to pay my account arrears and failure to respond to recent correspondence, they are issuing court proceedings against me. This unfortunately I can't ignore.

I wasn't busy at work this morning so went round to their office and demanded to speak to the manager. After waiting twenty minutes I was seen by a Mr Musselwhite who told me he was sure this was a computer error but he would look into it and call me back later that morning. By two thirty I had still heard nothing from him so returned to the West Shires office only to be told that he had gone off to Leeds two hours ago and wouldn't be back till Friday. "Can I get hold of him up there?" I asked the counter clerk. "I doubt if anyone will be able to get hold of him," she replied. "He's at a conference. On effective communication skills."

The assistant manager was also unavailable so I decided the only thing for it was to ring the number at the top of the letter. Perhaps inevitably it turned out to be a call centre, and it was no surprise at all for me to be advised that I was in a queue. Having been further told that my call would be taken as soon as possible. I eventually got through after two hours and approximately one hundred renditions of the opening bars of the Hallelujah Chorus.

I was spoken to by Julie – she displayed a marked reluctance to offer anything more – who told me she too was certain this was a computer error but she would look into it and call me back later that afternoon, and certainly well before eight when she finished work for the day. She also gave me a number to call her back on in case of any difficulties. By seven fifty I had heard nothing from her so I dialled the special number. To my relief, it was answered at once. "Is that Julie?" I asked. "I'll put you through," was the reply. Almost at once the sounds of G.F. Handel rent the air yet again followed by the advice that I was in a queue and my call would be taken as soon as possible. After half an hour I gave up.

I could only guess that Julie had gone off to Leeds as well, endeavouring to communicate more effectively with Mr Musselwhite and most if not all of the call centre staff. What is certain is that both my quarterly home and office phone bills will have trebled on the basis of this afternoon alone. And that if Tripplehorn decides to include the Hallelujah Chorus in next month's concert, I'm off to Nepal.

Thursday 25th April

Over breakfast, following a largely sleepless night, I was listening to our local radio station, Rustic FM, and quite fortuitously they announced that at four this afternoon on their drivetime show they would be doing one of their "Consumer Bites Back" slots. The purpose of these slots is apparently to highlight and where possible remedy problems suffered by consumers at the hands of shops and suppliers. Better still, they gave a telephone number "for your story of bumper bodge-ups by the big battalions." I called it straight away and, remarkably, got an answer almost immediately. I explained to the very nice girl, Lucy, what had happened and was told that someone would get back to me within the hour. I wasn't going to hold my breath, but almost as soon as I got into work I had Lucy on the phone saying that she would like me to appear on the programme that afternoon, as part of a special feature they were doing on call centres and the problems they caused to helpless consumers. She had also found an e-mail address for West Shires Building Society head office, and would hope to have the problem resolved within another couple of hours. An hour later, she had forwarded to me an e-mailed letter from West Shires Building Society stating the whole thing had been a computer mixup, advising me that the fault had now been rectified, apologising for the confusion, and assuring me of their best attention at all times including an offer to me to remortgage my property to them on very reasonable terms.

Which made sitting in an empty but hideously overheated studio above a Chinese takeaway in Rutherford Street staring at a dusty microphone telephone link with Rustic FM between 3.55pm and 6.20pm only to be told that my item had had to be squeezed out owing to the need for extended traffic bulletins following a major road closure owing to a three-vehicle pile up involving lorries filled respectively with Maris Piper potatoes and Dulux matt emulsion paint almost tolerable.

Friday 26th April

A good practice tonight, and made all the more enjoyable when Jane agreed to meet me afterwards for a drink to talk about duets for the concert. Over a most agreeable bottle of white wine we agreed a shortlist of five or six duets, and have arranged to meet again on Sunday at her mum's house. Her mum's partner, though no singer and no churchgoer, is apparently a fine accompanist.

After two or three glasses our tongues had loosened somewhat, and rather boldly, I asked her who she was seeing at the moment. She told me she'd had a couple of dates with Clive Halton, who'd been a co-leader with her of the church youth group but had since moved to a church ten miles away and seemed to have his finger in every pie there. "I don't think the relationship's going anywhere, to be honest," she said. "I mean, I don't want to knock what he does, but I can't see myself wanting to commit to some saddo whose idea of unwinding after a day's work is sitting for three hours in a PCC meeting." Not having officially agreed to join the PCC myself, I felt quite at liberty to reply that I couldn't agree more.

Whether or not it was the wine I don't know, but I felt quite amazingly turned on to Jane tonight. It seemed the most natural thing in the world to ask her back for a coffee at my house, and to my delight she agreed. We were just about to leave when Craig Dumbleton lurched across to us and after some totally unintelligible monologue concerning summer weekend engineering works in the Sevenoaks Tunnel, said "I gather congratulations are in order." I looked somewhat askance at him, so he went on "We need more young blokes like you on the PCC."

As if by magic, Jane decided she was a bit tired and could we skip coffee tonight.

From now on, Craig Dumbleton can sit next to Arthur Ramsbottom every Sunday and not just the first and third. Or better still, spend the next twelve Sundays stuck on a rail replacement bus service somewhere between Tunbridge Wells and Orpington.

Sunday 28th April – *FOURTH SUNDAY AFTER EASTER*

A more powerful sermon from our vicar than usual this morning, stressing the crucial importance of Christian discipleship, lamenting our woefully cavalier Western attitudes to our spiritual responsibilities, and accusing contemporary Western Christians of practising and presenting an over-diluted and excessively compromising faith in the face of the ever-burgeoning secularism around us. At least I think that's what was said. I was rather busy trying to remember whether I'd missed sufficient episodes of

EastEnders during the week to justify my staying in to watch today's omnibus edition.

The reference to Christian discipleship may or may not have been intended deliberately to address the serious shortage of nominees for the respective posts of PCC choir representative, honorary treasurer and keeper of the brass-cleaning roster, but as we blundered our way rather feebly through Brahms' *How Lovely Are Thy Dwellings* my conscience pricked me into finally deciding to put myself forward for the PCC membership. It may mean Jane demoting me in her log of objects of desire to only just above the drummer of the Bay City Rollers and only just below a bucketful of cold mashed potato, but I'm really not that bothered, especially having seen her flounce off after church this morning on the arm of a bloke who looked like a cross between Sid Vicious and the prehistoric ape-creature of Tanganyika.

Over coffee I quite stupidly told Henry Peasgood of my decision. "Well," he said, "Just as long as you don't want to change anything, you're welcome to it." I told him I understood that's what committees were for, especially if things weren't as we would like them to be. "Put it this way," he said, "Have you ever tried drinking a bowl of soup with a fork while walking blindfold up an escalator with ice-skates attached to your feet? But don't let me put you off." I might just as well have been talking to the Chinese speaking clock.

MAY

Wednesday 1st May

I am now officially choir representative on the PCC. It was nice being applauded by the assembled company at tonight's annual church meeting. The vicar spoke to me afterwards and expressed gratitude and delight that God should have appointed me out of all the choir members to further his work amongst the St Basil's faithful. It would indeed be nice to think that it was divine direction that had brought me my new position. Rather than the fact that nobody else in the choir would touch it with a bargepole.

As I was leaving, the PCC secretary, Mr Trimble, advised me that the first meeting of the new PCC would be in the vicarage next Tuesday evening, and said an agenda would follow in the post. Mr Gilliland, an existing member of the PCC, was hovering nearby, and I asked him if there was anything I needed to bring with me. "A hipflask and a sleeping bag," he told me. "You get a coffee when you arrive if you're lucky, and we never finish till gone ten thirty. Sometimes a great deal later. Twenty to midnight's not unusual."

Perhaps Tripplehorn was right on Sunday. When Rachel overheard him referring to me as "one piece of sticky back plastic short of a Blue Peter badge."

Friday 3rd May

I was in good spirits as I came home this evening, with a bank holiday weekend looming. My spirits were raised even more when Jane Markwick came on to the phone. "I'm surprised you should want anything to do with me now I'm on the PCC," I joked. "Yes, I'm sorry," she said. "I actually think it's really good that you're the choir rep. That Hazel Ledworthy never got anything done." She went on to say that she would love to meet me after rehearsal tonight, why didn't we go and have something to eat, and was the coffee invitation still open. I could hardly believe it. I almost danced to church for our practice.

Arrived to find Tripplehorn in a vile mood. When all were assembled he said "The concert's a fortnight tomorrow. I've just been told that six of you are away the whole of next weekend and five of you away the Friday after. We need two extra rehearsals at least. Can we all make the next two Wednesdays?" Then the fun started. Alison advised him that Wednesday was cubs and brownies night, ruling out all her family including herself as chauffeuse, whilst Queenie, Hazel and Eileen all announced that Wednesday night was bridge night and to even contemplate suggesting they cancel it was a step to be taken only by the insane or those with experience in mud-wrestling with crocodiles, kick-boxing with velociraptors or delivering consignments of Milk Tray to nubile young females. Mondays were impossible because Tripplehorn taught at the adult education institute and one was a bank holiday anyway, Tuesday was not only my first PCC but bell-ringers' night and, as Tripplehorn said, it would be easier to compete with a pack of baying wolfhounds on heat. That left Thursday; next Thursday was out because of Ascension Day, and as for the following Thursday it was the turn of the men to present their apologies, Irving Cattermole and Henry Peasgood having to attend rotary, Brian Ellis working late, and Craig Dumbleton at some other function which from the rather subdued and circumspect manner in which he announced it might have been a meeting of the local masonic lodge or that unmissable event of the year, the annual convention of the Hornby Double-Oh Appreciation Society.

Craig's excuse seemed to be the straw that broke the camel's back. Our choirmaster slammed down the psalter he was holding and said "Fine. We'll just have to try and get it all done tonight." I suppose Jane and I could have escaped, were it not for the fact that Craig left feeling unwell at half past eight and Jane would not only have incurred the displeasure of her mother but risked the eternal wrath of Cora Willoughby-Smith for stepping on her bunions. By ten twenty five, when we all decided we'd had enough, it was obvious that all the decent eateries in town would be shut. Hoping to make the best of a bad job, we decided on a Indian takeaway – only for Jane to meet five of her college friends there who persuaded her to go off to a club instead. Leaving me with an unusually large surplus of naan bread. And slightly less inclination than previously to join the Hornby Double-Oh Appreciation Society.

Sunday 5th May – *ROGATION SUNDAY*
Although Psalm 104 was quite a marathon with its thirty-five verses, it was worth it, with sumptuous chants by Bairstow and Howells and the quite magnificent words of thanksgiving for God's creation.

Met up with Jane at her house afterwards to do some duetting. Unfortunately she really wasn't in the mood to discuss the events of late Friday night which had really quite upset me – and not just because of the naan bread which is still cluttering up my freezer. While I was there Brian Ellis came on the phone and asked if we were interested in going out this afternoon to St Cuthbert's, Hook Newton for their traditional Rogation Sunday "beating the bounds" which would involve walking round the parish boundary and stopping on occasions for prayer and hymns. It's become traditional for our choir members to join them, owing to an obscure connection we have with them – Brian seems to think Queenie Haverthwaite's first cousin had a sister-in-law who worked for a man whose brother was married to the St Cuthbert's church cleaner. I think I've closer connections with the South West Irkutsk Tuesday Afternoon Over Sixties Tractor Maintenance Co-Operative, but still.

Jane clearly unkeen, but I thought it sounded quite fun and said I'd go. Immediately she said "So you're not wanting to come out with me this afternoon." I said I didn't think she seemed in the mood for going out anywhere but if she wanted me to take her out, I'd be delighted. "Oh, no," she said. "You've made other arrangements now. I might pop round later. If you're not too busy washing the carpet of your kitchen cupboard." In the circumstances, it probably is just as well that we've ditched the kissing duet from *The Mikado*.

There was quite a sizeable gathering at three o'clock outside St Cuthbert's, on what was quite a perfect spring afternoon. Although we were told we wouldn't be following the boundary exactly – just as well perhaps, as part of it ran through an electricity substation and another part through a sewage works – we would stay as close to it as possible, making strategic stops to pray and sing. Unfortunately, although the vicar had a goodly supply of prayers, we soon began to run short of hymns that we all knew and which were somehow relevant to the countryside. It was also slightly worrying that in the absence of a tuning fork or pitch pipe, I was being relied upon to find the right notes, and thus having to take the blame every time the sopranos were having to shrill or the basses having to growl. Having got through the obvious hymns – *All Things Bright And Beautiful, For The Beauty Of The Earth, O Worship The King, Let Us With A Gladsome Mind* – we began to struggle. A field of lambs sent us enthusiastically into *Loving Shepherd Of Thy Sheep*, and a field of young corn prompted a rendition of *Fair Waved The Golden Corn* (notwithstanding the fact that the verse continued "in Canaan's pleasant land"), but mercifully the sight of Newton Cap, the fine viewpoint in the vicinity, did not prompt anyone to suggest we launch into *From Greenland's Icy Mountains*. Having been held up on the way home by a herd of cattle being led across the road in front of us – nobody thankfully being tempted to suggest the hymn with the line "prowling beasts about thy way" – we enjoyed a quite sumptuous spread at Manor Farm House by the church. Refreshed and replete from delectable cheese scones, freshly-made farmhouse bread, fluffy sandwiches with choice slices of ham and beef, and quite heavenly iced rich fruit cake, I got back to town far later than I expected.

Literally seconds after I got indoors, the doorbell rang. It was Jane. She gave me a big smile and said "I've come to apologise for earlier. I was way out of....." She broke off and sniffed the air keenly, then demanded "What is that foul smell?" I tried to explain that we had been walking in the country for much of the afternoon, and I simply hadn't the time to take my boots off. She replied "I'm sure there are lots of girls that find the aroma of Gortex mingled with Hook Newton sewage a real turn on. But it doesn't do a lot for me. See you."

And as if that wasn't enough, I find I'm right out of carpet shampoo.

Tuesday 7th May

Got an e-mail from Tripplehorn asking if at tonight's meeting I could put in a request for funding for the provision of new choir folders and new robes for the Sparkes children.

I imagined my chance would come under Item 6, headed Reports From Areas Of Responsibility, but when I mentioned it – speaking up for the first time in the meeting – the chairman rather brusquely said that should properly come under A.O.B. which was item 12 at the end of the agenda. Under the circumstances, although unlike everyone else present I had a job to go to next day, I felt I had no alternative but to sit it out till then. Having cantered through the first ten items by nine thirty, we seemed on course for a civilised finishing time, and I was confident of getting home for *Newsnight*, if not *Have I Got News For You*. Then, however, the chairman announced "Item 10 – church heating – which is what I think we need to concentrate on for the bulk of tonight's meeting." To my horror, a Mr Ballantyne-Glazebrook, who like me had contributed virtually nothing to proceedings thus far, produced from his briefcase copies of numerous documents detailing new heating systems for the church, complete with costings. It meant as much to me as the Magna Carta would to a dysfunctional Ninja turtle, but evidently others were far more *au fait* with the issues and it was not until twenty five past eleven that discussion on it ceased, the unanimous decision being.....to refer the whole matter to a sub-committee with a view to reporting back to the next meeting.

Fortunately Item 11 – "To note the appointment of Mrs Bagwell on to the 2008 Altar Cloth Centenary Celebration Steering Group" – took all of thirty seconds, but typically I was the last person called upon to contribute items of any other business and by then it was ten minutes past midnight. Deciding that discretion was the better part of valour, I agreed my items could probably wait till the next meeting in eight weeks' time. Staggered home to find *Newsnight* had long finished and that my television choice to accompany my much-needed milky coffee and Wispa bar consisted of Godzilla meeting King Kong, women's league baseball from South Dakota, the effect of El Nino on tomato planting in Venezuela, and instructions on how to make soft toys out of empty crisp packets.

Thursday 9th May – *ASCENSION DAY*

Tripplehorn rang me early on. I assumed this was to find out how the PCC had gone, so I went into a long and somewhat grovelling apology and explanation. He let me talk for probably five minutes, then laughed and said "Don't worry, for goodness sake. I never expected you to get a result with that lot anyway. Enjoy the next year, won't you."

He went on to say he was actually asking if I could sing in this morning's primary schools' service in St Basil's, an Ascension Day tradition that goes back at least a century. There was a perk, he told me, namely that afterwards the parents and musicians have customarily joined the children in the church hall for a slap-up lunch. Reluctantly I had to decline. However, after this evening's Ascension Day mass, Rachel and Brian announced that because the caterers had prepared far too much food, and it would only go to waste otherwise, they were inviting choir members back to their house for a party to finish the grub. Margaret Pardew was there, and I made a point of going to chat to her, as I knew she'd been ill just recently. When at the end of the conversation she said "I feel so much better for our talk," I felt pleased and uplifted that I had managed to hold fast to the values that Jesus commanded us to maintain after he had ascended to be with his Father. In a burst of exuberance, I said to her with a laugh "As for that coronation chicken, I think Delia Smith's job's safe. I've eaten tastier curried manure." Her face turned pale and she replied "Actually, I cooked that myself."

Friday 10th May

We were a select band indeed for tonight's choir practice but made some good headway on most of the pieces. At the end Tripplehorn asked how the publicity was going. Joan Trumpington said "Actually, I spent the whole of today and yesterday going round town with posters and handbills. Could some of you take a few as well?" They were certainly very attractively designed and I imagine cost a fair bit to produce. GRAND CONCERT AT ST BASIL'S CHURCH, it read. RUTTER, BRAHMS, BRUKNER AND MUCH MORE. MAY 18TH. FOR TICKETS TELEPHONE 683950. "Super poster," Tripplehorn observed. "Colourful, eye-catching and succinct. I mean, okay, we're not doing anything by Bruckner. And even if we were, you don't spell his name like that. The phone number's wrong. Should be 683951. And you don't say what time it starts. Other than that, first class." Perhaps we should be grateful for small mercies. That firstly, she got the date and place right, and secondly that she didn't state the telephone number to be 683952. The number of the council mortuary.

Sunday 12th May – *SUNDAY AFTER ASCENSION*

Our vicar was preaching elsewhere this morning so the service was taken by an exceedingly doddery retired archdeacon. Beforehand, I overheard Tripplehorn say to Joan Trumpington "You have definitely told him to mention the concert in the notices, haven't you." "Oh yes," Joan replied. The archdeacon went out to speak to the congregation before we processed in, clutching the marriage banns book and the concert poster with the time now beautifully inscribed thereon and Bruckner's name discreetly removed. Despite his advancing years, the archdeacon preached extremely well but our performance of Holst's *Turn Back O Man*, which we are singing on Saturday, was so dreadful that we were ordered to stay on afterwards and do it again, properly. We just made it up to the hall in time for a cup of lukewarm coffee, but by then almost everyone else had gone. As the archdeacon was leaving, Tripplehorn said to him "I take it you did announce the concert before the service." "Oh yes," he replied. "I'm sorry I shan't be joining you myself but I told them all to come along and support you in droves – next Sunday evening."
Brilliant.
Tripplehorn was all for us going round to the house of everyone in the parish who was included on the electoral roll with a notification of the correct date. I suggested a more effective and efficient alternative strategy might be to get something in this week's local rag. "It's all right," Joan volunteered. "I wrote a press release last week and sent it to Arthur Batsford at his home. He always includes anything I write." As a belt and braces precaution, I went round to my office after lunch and e-mailed a press release of my own. Back came a reply almost at once, saying that sadly the copy deadline for the entertainments page had come and gone, but if I'd like to telephone Robert Lavis at once he had another suggestion to make. When I got him, he said he was friendly with Andy Juggins, who presents the late Sunday night show on Rustic FM, and he was sure Andy would give us a mention, but couldn't guarantee it. "Never mind," I said. "Anyway, our choir secretary did say she'd sent a press release to Arthur Batsford." "That's a shame," Robert Lavis replied. "He died two years ago."

Wednesday 15th May

Was supposed to be spending this evening going over my duets with Jane but as I was about to go out to see her she rang and said that she felt it would be better if they were cancelled. Apparently she thought she might have a cold coming on. Or so she said.

Moments later Joan Trumpington was on the phone asking how many tickets I'd sold. I told her at the rate I was going I'd be lucky to sell zero. She told me not to despair because somehow the piece she sent to the late Arthur Batsford has found its way into the paper. I didn't like to ask how.

It was a lovely evening so I decided to walk to the newsagent and buy a copy of the paper to see for myself. I happened to see Lesley there and sympathised with her over Jane's sudden cold. "I wouldn't," she said. "Let's just say something came up." "What's that?" I enquired. "I think she's going fly-fishing at Walton on the Naze," said Lesley. "Either that or watching rugby in Stoke D'Abernon. I don't think she knows herself."

Sure enough there was a nice little piece about a concert, taking place on.....Saturday 18th *June*. I pointed out to Lesley the latest marketing ploy Joan had devised to ensure our concert enjoyed no support whatsoever. "Oh, yes, I did see that," she said casually. "I did point it out to her when she rang earlier, but she said she thought people would assume it was this Saturday because if they checked their diaries they'd see 18th June wasn't a Saturday but a Tuesday when let's face it it's unlikely a concert would be taking place and anyway the press never tend to advertise anything that far ahead unless the circumstances are quite exceptional."

Eat your heart out, Albert Einstein.

Friday 17th May

We spent some time tonight deciding whether we should actually do the concert at all, bearing in mind that Joan Trumpington as well as Jane Markwick have now cried off, and only twelve people appear to have bought tickets. Of those twelve, three may or may not turn up depending on the availability of a babysitter, Cora's sister won't want to come out if it's too cold or too wet, and Queenie's cousin won't want to come out if it's too hot.

"I've sung a concert in front of only six people before," Craig Dumbleton volunteered.

"When we did Maunder's *Olivet To Calvary* at half past eight on Good Friday evening during a thunderstorm," said Arthur Ramsbottom, "we got an audience of four."

"If it comes to that," said Henry Peasgood, "I've sung a concert in front of two. And I think both of them were just sheltering from the rain until the 14 bus turned up."

"Well, I think we should do it," said Margaret. "We should remember we sing to the glory of God and principally for his benefit."

"Shame you can't sell him a ticket then, isn't it," said Tripplehorn. Whereupon poor Margaret dissolved into tears and hurried outside.

As if stung by her quite understandable reaction, Tripplehorn sighed and said "Oh, all right, we'll do it. On the condition that Joan Trumpington has no part in organising the next concert. At least now I've got the pretext I need to keep her out of harm's way. I frankly doubt if she'll be able to organise herself to get to her own cremation. More's the pity."

I don't know how he gets away with it.

Saturday 18th May

Almost all day was spent in rehearsal, but in the knowledge that virtually nobody was going to turn up to watch us, there was little conviction in our singing – or indeed in the musical direction. Tripplehorn remarkably lax with us, failing to notice any of the mistakes we made in the Rutter and not even bothering to play a chord after we'd finished an unaccompanied piece to show us how many semitones we'd slipped. I half wondered if now he had a basis for forcing Joan Trumpington to relinquish her stranglehold on the choir's administrative affairs, nothing else in the world mattered to him. The last thing he said to us, taking care to avoid Margaret's eye, was "Just say a few prayers that somebody will turn up." You could have cut the gloom with a knife.

We went home for tea, and returned at seven fifteen to behold an amazing sight – a long line of people queuing down the church path. Amazingly, there were remarkably few zimmer frames amongst them, and one or two – indeed more than one or two – looked positively youthful. By the time we started, the church was virtually full. I recognised hardly any of the faces, but they were a kind and alert audience, with hardly a snore to be heard and no humming from the perenially defective loop system for the hard of hearing. We thought we must be dreaming.

At the end, we weren't so much congratulating ourselves on the money we'd made and the things we'd actually got right as how we'd managed to get such an amazing audience. Alison's eyes lit up and she said "Oh, it's very easy. There was a double booking. The infants school PTA bowling evening had to be cancelled because the Gramophone Society Annual Tea Dance had bagged the hall first. My husband persuaded the bowlers to come to us instead."

"Bravo, whoever was responsible for the double booking!" Tripplehorn cried. "They can have a drink on me any time. Who was it?" "Joan Trumpington," Alison replied.

Sunday 19th May – *PENTECOST*

If there's one thing more dispiriting than trying unsuccessfully to sell tickets for a concert, it's having your ear bent by people who the day after the concert were unable to make it for any number of unlikely reasons, from over-running garden fetes and rain-delayed cricket matches to the dramatic revelation that an aged aunt in Kirby Muxloe has gone down with tennis elbow.

Ken Foulkes was back in the congregation today, and while clearly looking quite weak still, he greeted us cheerfully before the service. We had a good congregation as we always do at Pentecost, perhaps because of the delicious party cake we traditionally enjoy afterwards – our vicar insists that because Pentecost marks the birthday of the Christian church, we should celebrate it accordingly. It's a good job nobody insisted on all the candles as well.

Our anthem this morning was Attwood's *Come Holy Ghost* which began with quite a substantial solo section, snapped up by Cora Willoughby-Smith. While there were fewer wrong notes than usual, and she didn't crack on all the high notes – she sang most of them down the octave anyway – it was still a very poor performance. Ken came up to us as we were guzzling our cake afterwards and whispered "Poor Cora doesn't get any better, does she?" "I never quite know what to say to her when she asks me what I thought of it," Rachel replied. "Oh, it's very easy," said Ken. "Just use W.S. Gilbert's formula.'Good isn't the word!!'"

Friday 24th May

Well, it's official. Ken Foulkes has decided to leave the choir after eighteen years' service, preceded by thirty years in a church choir in South London. His departure leaves the basses quite short: Brian is often away with work, Irving Cattermole has been doing a lot of filling-in on the organ in neighbouring churches recently, and Henry Peasgood, while considering himself to be God's gift to English church music, is neither as reliable or as tuneful as he obviously thinks he is.

We seemed to spend an interminable time discussing who might replace him. A number of names came up but in each case there seemed more than ample reason not to ask them. Mike Stringer would have been ideal had he not got a job that didn't finish till seven on Friday night in central London, making him unavailable for every practice; Martin Lancaster would have been eminently suitable if he did not spend his Sunday mornings supervising local offenders on community service placements; Stephen Vincent would have been a splendid choice but for his imminent retirement and move to Spain; and Rodney Shearwater was certainly available but, as Tripplehorn charitably remarked, had a voice like a rusty foghorn and was about as much use to the choir as a penny-farthing to a duck-billed platypus.

"There's always Raymond Stapley," said Craig doubtfully.

"I think not," said Lesley Markwick. "He's a born troublemaker. He reduced four of the cast to tears when he produced the nativity play the Christmas before last."

"Well, to be fair, the kids do get very easily upset," said Queenie Haverthwaite.

"Who's talking about kids?" said Lesley. "They were all grown men. And one of them was God."

Sunday 26th May – *TRINITY SUNDAY*

As I was lying in bed this morning I had our local radio Sunday Breakfast programme on. Listeners were being invited to enter a competition to compose an anthem for this year's Harvest Festival, the prize for the winning anthem being a substantial cheque, a performance in Winchester Cathedral in September and a radio airing in October. Without any significant composing experience I don't stand much chance, but it'll be fun to have a try. In my enthusiasm I actually managed to make a start before going off to church.

One of my favourite anthems at church this morning – Stainer's *I Saw The Lord*. True to form, Henry Peasgood scathingly dismissed it as a "bit of crass Victoriana" but I saw him bellowing that "the house was filled with smoke" as robustly as anybody else. It was a shame it happened to be two bars too early.

Tripplehorn asked us all to stay on afterwards as he had an important announcement to make. He told us that apparently the choir that was to be singing evensong at Salisbury Cathedral next Saturday has had to pull out, and would we like to take their place. If we're to do it, we'll need an extra rehearsal on Tuesday night and will also rehearse all Saturday afternoon in the cathedral itself.

A number of us, myself included, said we'd love to go. Typically, perhaps, it was Hazel Ledworthy who sounded a note of caution. "Well, I'm not sure we're really quite equal to it," she said. "We're a bass short, the psalm didn't go well this morning, and presumably we'll have to sing all the psalms appointed for the evening. Our robes need laundering and aren't due to go for another couple of weeks. We won't have time to get the music up to standard and there's the problem, isn't there, of how we're all going to get there. Some of us may have commitments next Saturday which will make it quite impossible for us all to make the start of the rehearsal. The acoustic at Salisbury is very peculiar. We've only sung there once or twice before. I'm honestly not entirely certain we're really up to it. It would have been nice to know much earlier. I think we need to consider this very carefully. Perhaps have an in-depth discussion tonight or tomorrow night and make an informed decision."

There was a thoughtful silence followed by a few sage nodding of heads.

"When must we let them know by?" Queenie asked.

"I told them yes last night," said Tripplehorn.

Tuesday 28th May

Just before I went out for the extra rehearsal tonight Jane Markwick rang. She's coming with us to Salisbury but is travelling down on the Friday evening to meet up with friends and would I like to join them, in exchange for providing transport for her, there and back. It'll mean having to endure some of their beloved garage music in one of the city's nightclubs and then sleeping on Gareth's floor, whoever Gareth may be, but she thinks I'll get on with her friends like a house on fire. I doubt it, considering that the only thing I appear to have in common with any of Jane's friends of my acquaintance is that we live in the same universe – and I wonder about that sometimes. A cynic might think I was being well and truly used, not only emotionally but as a cheap taxi service. But I do love Salisbury and it would be nice to have a Friday night out for once. I told her I'd think about it and ring her tomorrow.

Wisely, Tripplehorn has kept things reasonably simple for the Salisbury, but we can't avoid having to sing the psalms appointed for the first evening – 6,7 and 8. Psalm 6 contained the words "Each night wash I my bed" which as Tripplehorn reminded us was set to music by Herbert Bumfrey, but mercifully there was no suggestion that we should subject the poor innocent worshippers of Salisbury to it. We spent some time afterwards working out who was going to take who. Alison asked me if I was all right and I replied I wasn't sure. "Well, don't worry," she said. "I've got a spare seat in my car if you need. Margaret's coming with us and providing some musical backing but there's plenty of room for another."

"What musical backing's that?" I enquired. "Oh, the tape from her Praise Parade at Plumstead Common last week," Zoe informed me. "Hopefully it'll drown out Matthew being sick whenever we go round a corner. He's always sick on long journeys."
Gareth's floor, here I come.

Friday 31ˢᵗ May
With this being the start of the bank holiday weekend, I knew that the traffic was going to be horrendous so having carefully planned a route which I anticipated would avoid all the major snarl-ups, I asked Jane to be ready to meet me no later than three fifteen outside my house. I was delighted to get away from the office in excellent time but come 3.15, no Jane. Every minute we delayed was, I reckoned, going to cost us another ten minutes in travelling time. It was at twenty eight minutes past three that she finally showed up, explaining to me that she had only just managed to get off the phone to a friend of hers who lived what she described as "sort of" on the way and to whom she had promised to deliver an essay which may help her to pass a crucial exam on Wednesday. "Sort of" turned out to be a detour of a good twelve miles plus a delay of fifteen minutes when we got there. I suspect she sensed my irritation when she got back in the car, and she tried to make amends by suggesting a short cut back to my chosen route. The short cut soon plunged us into a spectacular traffic jam, the sheer tedium of waiting in which was not mitigated in the slightest by Jane switching on Radio 1 at full blast. I managed to find an escape route but was now so far off course from where I wanted to be that I was forced to approach the city from a completely different angle, grinding to another halt some nine miles from the city centre. It was a hot afternoon and my throat, to quote Tripplehorn on the last choir outing as video-ed by Arthur "Steven Spielberg....Not" Ramsbottom, felt as dry as John the Baptist's flip flops.
Fortunately a sign by a side turning promised a pub, the Watersmeet, three hundred yards down the road, so at my suggestion we decided to pay it a visit. A converted watermill, it had a beautiful setting, and was wonderfully snug and welcoming inside. The restaurant menu looked extremely tempting, and it struck me as an ideal place to go for a romantic meal. I went to the bar to order some drinks, having to queue behind a gaggle of other obviously frustrated motorists, and returned to find Jane engrossed in conversation with a man in his mid twenties who looked like a cross between a primitive Antipodean bushman and a New Age traveller having a bad hair day. He got up to leave as I came near, and Jane's parting words to him were "See you later."

79

The moment he'd gone, she gave me her classic all-too-familiar "It's blow-you-out time" look, and said to me "I can't believe it. That was Peter, one of my best mates. I met him when I was backpacking in Peru last year. He's off to Italy tomorrow for a whole year, travelling and working, and he's in Salisbury just for tonight, staying with his parents. I'm really sorry, but I would so love to spend the evening and tomorrow morning with him. His parents have said they'll put me up for the night. You don't mind, do you?"

"Not in the least," I lied. But my crestfallen expression must have been too obvious to her, because she went on "Look, I'm really sorry. We don't have to spoil our little holiday. How about tomorrow we go for a meal on the way home. Just us two. A nice romantic dinner. We could come here if you like. And it'll be my treat. My dad had a bit of a windfall the other week. I'll book it now. Their nicest table by the window overlooking the mill stream."

After that, and a very agreeable drink we enjoyed together, the one hour journey to complete the remaining eight and a half miles seemed a trifling inconvenience. Which was hardly an appropriate description for the twenty minutes I spent locating a car park, another forty trying to find the pub where Jane was meeting the bad-haired bushman, a further eighty to track down a hotel with a vacant room, and thirty to find a decent fish and chip shop. Returned to the hotel at half past ten reflecting that at least I wouldn't be subjected to garage music for the next few hours and then have to sleep on a floor. Instead, I lay sleeplessly in my damp and hideously uncomfortable bed in room 12 with raging indigestion until two forty five while a heavy metal band pounded away in the club next door. Not that that seemed to deter the snorer in room 11 or the amorous couple in room 13. Eventually I was forced to seek refuge in the one soundproof room in the place. The broom cupboard.

JUNE

Saturday 1ˢᵗ June

Following my quite wretched night in the hotel, a much pleasanter morning's window-shopping round the bustling centre of Salisbury.

The rehearsal in the stalls was at two thirty, and determined not to be late after missing last night's rehearsal, I arrived at the song school, where we were robing, in excellent time. Rachel and Brian were already there. "Horrendous rehearsal last night," said Rachel. "You and Jane were seriously missed. Zoe's got a stomach bug and won't be able to do it. Matthew was a pain all the way through. Frank Tripplehorn was being a right so-and-so as well, threatening summary execution for anyone who forgot to bring their music with them."

Suddenly, the dreadful realisation hit me. I had been looking at the music in bed last night, but in my anxiety to escape from my ghastly hotel room as quickly as possible, had no recollection whatsoever of packing it into my overnight bag this morning. My worst fears were confirmed a moment later when a search of my overnight bag revealed no more than my sponge bag and the clothes I'd been wearing yesterday. "Oh dear," Rachel smirked. "What's your preference then? The guillotine or boiling oil?" It was all very well for her to laugh.

I had no alternative but to rush back to the hotel, dodging the huge crowds of Saturday afternoon shoppers and tourists. At last I got there and explained to the receptionist what had happened. She waited until I had finished my speech then announced "I'm sorry. I only started here today. I'll ask someone else to help you." It was only after I had spoken to no less than three members of staff who appeared to boast a cumulative length of service of eleven working days and a combined IQ of minus three point six that at last I found someone who appeared to value his patrons more highly than a slab of mildewed toilet duck. Minutes later I was scurrying away with my precious folder of music which had actually been found down the side of the bed that I had forsaken for the broom cupboard in the early hours of this morning. No wonder I'd missed it.

Unfortunately by now it was twenty past three. From what I could overhear as I approached the stalls, Tripplehorn's patience was now as short as a guide to Belgian Eurovision Song Contest winners, and when he saw me he merely grimaced and pointed me to where I should be standing. They were evidently forging their way through Psalm 7 but it was quite unclear to me whether we were being split into two choirs and singing alternate verses or singing full throughout. I knew it was pointless asking Arthur, who just yells everything double *forte* regardless of whether he's supposed to be singing it or not, and Craig too seemed to be in a world of his own, perhaps mentally composing his monthly report for the Railway Station Buffet Bar Gastronomic Society. So I asked Matthew who happened to be directly in front of me. As he was explaining, I suddenly heard Tripplehorn bark "Right, that does it. Matthew, I told you one more word out of you and you wouldn't sing this afternoon. That was your last warning. Go and sit in the nave. You won't be singing this evening." I tried to intervene on his behalf but I might as well have been talking to a parsnip. Poor Matthew, now reduced to floods of tears, made his way out of the stalls.

Evensong was, despite Tripplehorn's mood, a great success – a good congregation including some supporters from our own church, and a first-class rendition of all our choir pieces especially the psalms.

Jane looked stunning, and apparently none the worse for wear after yesterday's nightmarish journey. As we prepared to go back to the song school afterwards to disrobe, she patted my hand and said "Can't wait for tonight, lover boy." I just couldn't believe my good fortune. She seemed really keen to talk to me about her time with Peter last night, so at my suggestion, as the refectory was shut, we went for a wander round the cathedral. Although her progress was slightly hampered by her very chunky high-heeled sandals – I just didn't know how she'd got her feet into them, or was able to move around in them – she certainly caught the admiring eyes of many other visitors. I felt higher than the hosts of angels looking down from the lofty stained glass. It was good to hear that although she is very fond of Peter, he is already hitched – to a hairdresser in Reggio di Calabria, to wit. "A swarthy Southern European beauty, then!" I exclaimed. "Well, I'd hardly say that," she replied. "Though I've seen a picture of Marco and he is very good-looking."

So that's all right then.

At length we arrived back at the song school to find Alison standing outside it looking as though her numbers had come up on the lottery but she'd forgotten to buy the ticket. I asked her what the matter was. "Unbelievable," she said. "Our car won't start. I've got a car full and all my passengers and I are stranded. Everyone else has gone. The RAC'll be here in an hour but I really need to get the others home." We made the usual sympathetic noises. She went on "I could probably just about have stood it if we'd all enjoyed ourselves. But of course Frank Tripplehorn had to ruin it all by throwing Matthew out of the service. Matthew's so upset. It wasn't even his fault. It was only because someone else asked him something. He won't say who but I'd love to get my hands on them."

Under the circumstances, as the one responsible for Matthew's undeserved punishment, I felt duty bound to offer my services. I saw Jane turning away in disgust, which was understandable, but I saw no reason for her to react to my suggestion that we forgo the Watersmeet and go for a meal in town on our return with as much enthusiasm as if I were suggesting a barbecue on the concourse of Cleethorpes Bus Station.

Then again, at that stage I didn't know who my passengers were.

It may have been Craig Dumbleton identifying and then providing a history lesson on every piece of railway line, existent or disused, that we passed on our way home. It may have been Margaret Pardew's insistence on playing the same track from her Praise Be To Plumstead Common, or whatever it was, no less than eight times, and exhorting us to join in with the umpteen repeats of the principal refrain until I honestly wondered if I had become the victim of an updated version of the Chinese water torture. I personally think the clincher was Matthew depositing regurgitated versions of his Burger King elevenses and Macdonalds lunch partially over Jane's bare knees with the rest going on her brand new skirt. Suffice it to say that my evening was not spent enjoying an intimate candle-lit repast with the girl of my dreams. But at home alone with a boil-in-the-bag beef and dumplings in front of *You've Been Framed*.

Minus my overnight bag, complete with all my music, that I'd managed to leave behind in Salisbury.

Sunday 2nd June – *FIRST SUNDAY AFTER TRINITY*

Every cloud has a silver lining. Alison came up to me before the service this morning and gave me a big hug and a huge box of chocolates as a thank you for last night.

Ken Foulkes cornered me over coffee afterwards and reminded me about next Saturday's wedding at which about half the choir will be singing and to which I too had promised some weeks ago to lend my voice. He also reminded me that I'd agreed to attend a rehearsal for it at his house this evening, which I had completely forgotten about.

After the shattering day yesterday I really could have done with an evening in, especially as I was anxious to get some more work done on my Harvest anthem, but once I'd hauled myself out of my armchair and made my way to Ken's house, I felt altogether more positive about the whole thing. Ken had certainly handpicked his forces, namely Brian, Rachel, Margaret, Lesley, Jane, Alison and Irving, plus a friend of Ken's named Martin who used to be a professional opera singer and still is in considerable demand as a soloist in London where he lives. He joined me on tenor, while Ken himself, although no longer a choir member, sang with the basses. It was a treat for me to sing with such an accomplished musician as Martin, and the sound we made collectively was really quite exciting. The wedding is at the same church as the one Jane and I had visited on that disastrous Good Friday evening, and together with the reception promises to be an extremely glamorous affair – I understand the bride is something of a minor celebrity in the showbiz world – and certainly out of the normal St Basil's league. Tripplehorn has often commented that you can divide the St Basil's weddings into "proper church weddings" for people who regularly attend the church and participate fully in church life, weddings of relatives or close friends of regular church attenders who might come back and see us every so often but play no real part in the life and work of the church, and "twenty quid jobs" where we come in and sing, get our cash, make our escape before the crush, then don't see the couple again. Unless we're asked to bury them, that is.

Friday 7th June

Made an absolutely fatal mistake tonight. Having worked through most of last night and a considerable amount of my day off today to get the first draft of my Harvest anthem finished, was so desperate to get a second opinion on it that I took it to choir tonight to run past Tripplehorn. He played through it, not always completely accurately, and then turned to me and said "Do you want me to be polite or frank?" I didn't feel ready for a put-down so I opted for politeness. "Well," he said, "it's extremely novel and imaginative, and you've obviously put a lot of effort into it."
For a moment I felt quite pleased and proud, until Rachel nudged me and said "That's exactly how he described Queenie Haverthwaite's haddock and cabbage fritters." "But I thought half the congregation went down with food poisoning after eating them," I said. "Precisely," said Rachel.

Saturday 8th June

Ken was on the phone early saying he had some exciting news for us regarding the wedding. Apparently the bride and groom would like to be serenaded at tonight's reception at the bride's parents' large country home, and in return for providing some additional musical entertainment, consisting of a few straightforward madrigals, we are invited to join the guests for the occasion. "This could be very big for the choir of St Basil's," said Ken. "I know it's only half of you, but anything that gets us on the map has to be very good news." He's said for a long time that once the oldies are out of the way we will be left with a choir that could compete with some of

84

the best musical groups around, and in demand for further functions of this sort.

As I arrived at the church, I saw Jane get out of a car in front and give a protracted hug and kiss to a young man sitting in the driver's seat. While obviously disappointed that her fickle affections have clearly once again been transferred away from my direction, I at least didn't feel I needed to stand on ceremony for her tonight.

The church was absolutely packed solid for the 5pm wedding. But by twenty to six the bride had still not appeared, and everyone was beginning to look a little uneasy, not least the organist, who it was clear was running short of scheduled material and was now embarking upon what appeared to be a *Fantasy On Soap Opera Themes.*

"I wouldn't worry too much," said Ken philosophically. "My wife was over half an hour late."

"I seem to remember being at least forty minutes late," Alison giggled.

"My wife was five minutes early," mused the divorced Irving Cattermole. "I'm sorry she turned up at all."

It was nearly ten to six when at last the bride appeared. The service was not overlong, and it all proceeded so flawlessly and enjoyably that the time passed quickly. But, with an inevitably very long and tedious photo session afterwards in the sultry evening air, it was nearly half past seven when we all got into the cars to adjourn the twelve miles to the reception, and at ten past nine we were still shuffling around in a suffocatingly small Garden Room sipping Bucks Fizz. I saw Jane standing around looking extremely bored, but I do have some pride and I wasn't going to fall for it, preferring instead to chat to Rachel and Brian who like me saw this evening stretching ahead for ever. It wasn't till gone half past nine that we were invited to take our seats for the meal which judging by the speed, or lack of it, at which the first course was served appeared likely to be still going when Tripplehorn was expecting us at St Basil's for our Sunday worship. Quite how I managed to end up with Irving Cattermole on one side of me and Margaret Pardew on the other I cannot think. I am not entirely sure who was more painful to listen to: Irving, uttering disparaging remarks about everything from the temperature of the plate for his bread roll to the colour of the bride's mother's lipstick, or Margaret enthusing about her forthcoming week away at a Christian music co-operative that had been established in a disused railway carriage just outside Pontefract.

As we were eating our crème brulee at just gone twenty past eleven, I asked Ken when we were likely to be asked to sing, as I for one was hoping to go to bed that night. Ken assured me that as soon as we had finished our dessert, and before coffee was served, we would be providing our musical contribution and could then disperse if we wished to. No sooner had he spoken than there was a deafening crash of sound from the corner of the room, signifying that the band was ready to play. There followed a succession of short but very loud "big band" pieces, with minimal gaps between each, and people having finished their desserts were beginning to adjourn on to the nearby dance floor. I threw an appealing glance at Ken who promptly disappeared, returning some ten minutes later with the news that all the timings were out of kilter, and in the light of this we were now being asked to sing our pieces in the hallway leading from the main reception area to the terrace garden, presumably for the benefit of those wishing to avail themselves of the night air. It was perhaps unfortunate that not only did a torrential thunderstorm break at that moment, deterring guests from sampling the delights of the terrace garden, but the noise of the band was so deafening that the plaintive protestations of Phyllis and the woeful wanderings of Amyntas were completely submerged by the booming brass of the *Chatanooga Choo Choo*. When our sixth piece had come and gone with an enthusiasm that might be accorded by an anorexic grasshopper to a quarterpounder with cheese and large fries, we decided to call it a day, and made a hasty departure without bidding farewell to the bride whose tardiness had been responsible for the collapse of the planned schedule. Not that we had managed to establish the nature of her celebrity status, despite the seemingly interminable wait. Opinion was divided between two lines as a court usher in an episode of *Brookside* fourteen years ago and late night voice-over programme links on a cable TV station devoted exclusively to 1960's US situation comedies and available only to residents of Chorlton-cum-Hardy. So maybe we were a little over-optimistic in thinking we would make the back page of the *West Shires Evening Chronicle*, let alone the front cover of *Hello* magazine. Or that our performance would render our chances of achieving local fame as an up-and-coming *a cappella* group any bigger than a Trappist monk's address book.

As we walked purposefully back towards the car park, the rain beating like stair-rods on our umbrellas, Jane turned to me and said "You okay tonight? You seem a bit off. I was really looking forward to spending some time with you."

"As much time as that guy you were snogging before you came into church?" I asked her, as I opened the door of my car.

"Of course," said Jane, "but it's not every day my brother flies in from Santiago. See you."

Perhaps I'll stick to twenty quid jobs in future.

Sunday 9th June – *SECOND SUNDAY AFTER TRINITY*

The anthem today, Crotch's *Comfort O Lord The Soul Of Thy Servant*, could hardly have been more appropriate in the light of my mood this morning. As if last night's dollop of sackcloth and ashes had not been enough, another massive helping was on offer this morning, firstly with the news that Jane has been offered a summer job in France which would take her away from St Basil's from the end of June until the time she starts at college, and secondly a reminder that the parish fete is to take place on 22nd June and the choir is, as usual, being asked to man the car park and bottle stall, and provide helpers at seven that morning to help load and unload trestle tables and chairs, ready for the festivities to start at twelve noon.

"Just think, it could be worse," said Alison, who was hovering nearby with Matthew. "You could have got roped into the bonniest baby competition or the exemption dog show." True, but the prospect of losing my one decent lie-in of the week was perfectly gloomy enough on its own. Not to mention the fact that I have been arbitrarily rota'ed by Ernie Fincham, this year's co-ordinator, to be on duty at the stall between 2.45pm and 3.30pm, thus messing my afternoon up as well. "And I think I'm with Joan Trumpington and Hazel Ledworthy," I lamented. "You have got the dog show after all, then, haven't you," Matthew replied. It was the only time I felt like laughing all morning.

Wednesday 12th June

Got a phone call from Jane at work today, this after my trying unsuccessfully to contact her during the past three nights. Reading between the lines, I can't help thinking that my abject failure to establish an ongoing relationship with her was a major factor in her decision to look for work abroad. Especially when I asked her if her mind was made up, and she replied "That rather depends on you."

"Okay," I said, seizing the moment. "Let's go out together for lunch on Sunday. And then a nice walk and back to my house after that for tea."

"Is that really the best you can do?" she said. I started to splutter a response only to find I was talking to myself. I decided there was little point in my calling her back. That is, until I've arranged a six course lunch on Concorde en route to a safari through the Serengeti on bejewelled elephants.

Friday 14th June

The post today brought a letter from the vicar to me in my capacity as choir representative of the PCC. At the next meeting of the PCC, to take place on 2nd July, there's to be discussion about the adoption of a newly-published hymn book, *Kingdom Praise*, in place of the *New English Hymnal* which has served us for the last thirteen years. The choir has been asked for its views, but the vicar is very keen.

Tripplehorn had unlike me been favoured with a copy, and passed it round at tonight's practice.

"It certainly smells nice," said Lesley.

"Pretty picture on the cover," said Alison.

"Pages are a bit thin," said Irving Cattermole.

"The print's too small," said Cora Willoughby-Smith.

"I don't like it all being in alphabetical order," said Queenie Haverthwaite. "Much harder to find things." Nobody seemed to have the heart to mention that she's incapable of finding a hymn anyway until we're on to verse two.

"I agree," said Joan Trumpington. "You know where you are when all the Christmas carols and Easter hymns are together. I think the congregation will get confused. If they see 372, they know that means *Immortal Invisible*. 373, *Fill Thou My Life*. 374, *Stand Up And Bless The Lord*."

"That's *Ancient and Modern, Revised*," Craig Dumbleton reminded her. "Which we stopped using in 1975."

"I like it," said Margaret. "There's some in here I've wanted to sing for ages."

"Oh, if you're into all that happy-clappy stuff, it's wonderful," said Tripplehorn. "Personally, I think the congregation who turn up on a Sunday morning are entitled to sing something with a bit of profundity, the writers having given serious thought and time to every word of their composition, than having their intelligence insulted with something that could have been written within the space of one visit to the bog."

I can see the vicar's going to have a job to sell this one.

Sunday 16th June – THIRD SUNDAY AFTER TRINITY

Jane announced that this was to be her final Sunday in the choir. She's spending from tomorrow until next Sunday in Yorkshire with her father before setting off to France on the 30th, ready to start her job on the French Riviera on July 1st. Then she starts at Hull University on her return to England.

"Reminds me of that wretched joke," Craig Dumbleton commented to me as we lined up to start the service. "Man walks into pub and says 'I say I say I say! I've just been on holiday in the South of France.' 'Toulouse?' 'No, just the one! We only had an apartment!'"

Judging by the reaction of some of the younger members in the choir, the joke obviously isn't as old as I thought it was.

88

Jane had asked for two of her favourite hymns, *Lord Of The Dance* and *Morning Has Broken*, her favourite anthem, Bach's *Jesu Joy Of Man's Desiring*, and her favourite psalm, 65 – and we did more than ample justice to all of them. The vicar included a special mention for her in the intercessions. Seeing her standing there, confident, self-assured and devastatingly good-looking, she was unrecognisable from the gauche rather meek youngster who had co-led the church's youth group, and I can well understand her desire to wreak painful revenge on anyone unwise enough to exhibit for general display the photo of her on her confirmation day with her plaited hair, tooth-brace, gingham dress and long white socks.

I made a bee-line for her after the service to ask her to spend the afternoon with me. During the sermon I had visualised a farewell walk for us, perhaps on Inkbarrow Hill, which she had once said she found a romantic as well as a beautiful spot. A soft, balmy early summer evening with the never-changing vista of tree-clad hills and rolling fields before us, and azure skies and light wispy clouds looking down upon us, as we pledged to keep alive our fondness for each other which might yet be transformed into the unquenchable zeal of eternal love.

"Sorry," she said, "I'm washing my hair."

Was tempted to agree with Irving that if I heard Matthew tell that Toulouse joke once more, a tooth-brace would be the least of his dental worries.

Tuesday 18th June

As choir rep for the PCC, found myself being dragged along tonight for a fete planning meeting. Ernie Fincham, who chaired it, made Joan Trumpington at her worst appear a model of Teutonic efficiency. It appears that not a single choir member except myself and Arthur Ramsbottom are available for the morning's loading and unloading, and that although the cricket club are lending us the trestle tables and chairs, the club caretaker wasn't told anything about our arrangements till six last night and has arranged to be out from half past seven on Saturday. And there's no chance of getting it done the night before as the van that we're using is not expected back from France until half past eleven on Friday night. By the time we'd sorted out the logistics of that, the first of eighteen separate action points that had to be discussed, it was twenty to nine. I felt like a passenger trapped in a very slow stopping train that had got stuck in the first station.

We had staggered through to point eighteen, reaching it at ten past eleven after half a dozen signal failures, a couple of minor derailments and leaves on the line at West Dulwich, when Mavis Beechfield asked "Where do we go if it rains?" Ernie Fincham replied "The church hall of course, as always." Mavis looked in her diary and said "I think not. It's the scout bring and buy sale there on Saturday. They've had it in the diary for months and there's no way they'll agree to cancel."

Even British Rail was never that bad.

Friday 21st June

Tripplehorn announced he would be away for three Sundays in August; a chance, he said rather cruelly, to take a well-earned rest from us lot and service his earplugs. He said he didn't know who'd be playing instead but there's no guarantee they'll be up to playing any more than a simple voluntary and four hymns with tunes consisting of no more than two sharps or two flats apiece. "It's my turn to take mother to Weston-super-Mare," he explained. Then, mischievously feasting his eyes on Joan Trumpington, he went on "Of course, I'd far rather be with you."

What's so sad is that she probably believes it.

We had a new recruit in the choir tonight, by the name of Gordon Hunnisett. I should have feared the worst when I asked him whether he was a tenor or bass and he replied "A bit of both, I think," before announcing that the only audience for any singing he has done in his life has been the rubber ducks in his bath. And judging by the sounds that came out of his mouth, I shouldn't be surprised if even they have now got bits of cotton wool permanently lodged in their aural cavities.

Saturday 22nd June

Arrived at the cricket pavilion promptly at seven to collect the trestle tables, only to find that our deputation of willing choir helpers, notwithstanding a plea at the practice last night, consisted of just three people, namely myself plus Arthur Ramsbottom and his friend Harold. There was no sign of the van at all, and for the next hour and a quarter I was treated by Arthur to the most tedious monologue imaginable on the subject of his battle with the Happy Camcorder Company following their alleged refusal to replace the faulty filming equipment he'd bought from them six months ago. The caretaker was there as well, making it quite clear, during Arthur's all-too-infrequent pauses for breath, that he had put his back out last week while washing the pavilion roof and would be unable to lend any assistance when the van did finally appear. Fortunately he seemed happy to entrust a key to us and disappeared shortly before eight. It was a good half an hour later, as Arthur was reading the first draft of his letter of official complaint to the manager of the Happy Camcorder Company, duly copied to his local MP, his Euro MP, the Office of Fair Trading, the Ombudsman, the BBC *Watchdog* programme and Esther Ranson (sic), that the van finally did arrive. Only for us to find that caretaker hadn't given us the key to the cupboard within the pavilion that contained the trestle tables and chairs and was now on a coach heading for Glasgow.

It was only then that Harold, whose verbal contribution to the proceedings thus far had consisted of the two words "Bless you" when Arthur had sneezed in the middle of his diatribe about the sharp practices of camcorder dealers, mentioned that he knew a couple of cricket club members who would be likely to know somebody with easy access to a pavilion cupboard key. Following a couple of phone calls, five members of the cricket club arrived and did all the loading and subsequent unloading themselves. They had the whole thing done in 15 minutes without the need for the van. "Shame you didn't think of us earlier," a tall moustachio-ed cricketer said as the final trestle table slid out of the back of his Mitsubishi estate. "I told my auntie we'd be up here today and could do all this for you ourselves. You may know her. Joan Trumpington."

The next job was assisting Henry Peasgood with the car park marshalling, but since the fete wasn't due to start till 12 noon and the only cars coming in belonged to helpers, I spent most of the next two hours feeling as useful as a pork pie at a vegetarian convention. I did at least learn the three Church Fete Parking Laws. Law 1 – Henry Peasgood decides who parks where and nobody else. Law 2 – if any other mortal attempts to offer to Henry Peasgood a second opinion about his allocation policy, expect either a few ill-chosen words of contempt, or a stare as cold and hard as the seat in a Leningrad bus shelter on a Sunday morning in January. Law 3 – if Henry Peasgood likes you, expect to be allocated the plum parking spot immediately adjacent to the main marquee, and possibly a hand in getting you and your passengers out of your vehicle. If he doesn't, resign yourself to a walk back from your car to the fete ground which could be a brisk 15-minute march from the end of Lady Ponsonby's Passage or a six hundred mile hike through the Amazonian rain forests.

At a quarter to three, it was time to do my stint at the bottle stall. When I arrived, fresh from viewing for myself the defects in Arthur Ramsbottom's camcorder, Joan Trumpington and Hazel Ledworthy were sitting there looking as unmovable and unyielding as the Rock of Gibraltar, and reacted to my announcement that I had come to relieve them with no less surprise than I'd expected if I'd just been beamed down from the planet Jupiter in a luminous jumpsuit and fishermen's galoshes. They told me that there must be some mistake, that they and they alone had manned the 2.00pm to 3.30pm slot on the bottle stall every fete day since 1968, that they could manage perfectly well on their own thank you very much, and that if I'd nothing better to do I could always take over the fishing-for-chocolate-bars-out-of-paddling-pool stall and relieve Mrs Bletherington, who was suffering with a bad attack of housemaid's knee.

At that point I decided to leave and salvage of the day what I could. Unfortunately, as I was making my way towards the exit, I met Ernie Fincham. "Problem, I'm afraid," he said. "Cricket club members can't help us this evening, and three people who promised to help have just this second let me down. Any chance you can be back at five thirty sharp to reload and return the trestle tables and chairs? Shouldn't take long. Sooner we start, sooner we can all get away." I duly returned on the dot of 5.30 as requested, to find that they hadn't even started judging the bonniest baby contest or announced the winner of the competition to guess how many drawing pins there were in Owen Grimthorpe's wellington boot, and it was only at ten to seven that the last of the paying customers left and we were able to make a start on reloading. Or would have been, had we not then discovered that the van was out on a job. Forty miles away.

As I made my way home at twenty to ten, I reflected that at least some good had come out of the day. I may have wasted a perfectly good and much needed half of my weekend. I may have strained a muscle and got splinters in at least three of my fingernails when lifting my quota of trestle tables into the van. And I may have upset Ernie Fincham by telling one of the other helpers that I thought he had all the fete-running skills of a bowl of semi-digested tapioca only to discover he was right behind me when I said it. But at least now I know where not to buy a new camcorder should I ever want one. And Arthur Ramsbottom knows whom to turn to should Esther Ranson require supporting evidence as to the quality of his apparatus.

Sunday 23rd June – *FOURTH SUNDAY AFTER TRINITY*

One inescapable fact of life of a parish church of a country town is the high percentage of elderly people in the congregation, and therefore a large number of parishioners who are sick or dying at any one time. The list of sick people in the intercessions – or as Tripplehorn rather irreverently puts it, our Death Row Society – does seem to get longer and longer every week, to the extent whereby one or two people have suggested we should instead name the ever-dwindling number of people whose robust good health means they DON'T actually require to be prayed for.

Still, one person who has been on the sick list for years, Jack Lacey, has finally passed away. His funeral is taking place in the North, but as he was a regular here for most of his life, it was regarded as appropriate that his

92

passing be marked in some way. Accordingly, we rather boldly sang Bainton's *And I Saw A New Heaven*, one of the most technically demanding pieces in our repertoire, as the anthem. I completely missed the tricky tenor entry at "And God shall wipe all tears from their eyes" and neither Craig nor Arthur hit it either. Gordon Hunnisett was I think trying to sing the soprano part an octave lower and was likewise nowhere near the plot. Tripplehorn, who had had to bail the altos out a few bars previously, fortunately anticipated the problem and sang in the entry himself. Over coffee afterwards he remarked "I didn't mind covering up for you this morning, but I don't know how you're going to manage when I'm not here in August. Especially now the vicar's told me who's coming instead." "Who's that?" Brian enquired. "It's Arnold Petherbridge," Tripplehorn replied, "whose trademark is falling asleep in the sermon." "That's not unusual, surely," I said. "It is when he starts playing the offertory hymn at the same time," said Tripplehorn.

Friday 28th June

A shorter practice tonight. It was a very hot evening, the church was stuffy, and nobody felt much like singing. Afterwards, at Alison's suggestion, we all adjourned back to her garden for some welcome cold drinks and spent some time discussing first the new hymn books and then the choir summer party.

Tripplehorn has told the vicar he will be happy to use the new books one service a month on the condition that he withdraws the choir on that Sunday and we sing evensong that day instead. My understanding is that the vicar either wants to use the new books all the time or not at all, but at least there seems to be some dialogue going, which is more than could be said last week.

"There are advantages to doing a monthly evensong," said Tripplehorn. "We can use the prayer book psalm translations and get away from the awful modern ones. We can learn some evening service settings and thus broaden our repertoire. And there are some lovely evening hymns."

"There is one drawback," observed Alison. "Nobody will turn up."

"You don't know that," said Tripplehorn.

"Well, evensong was scrapped a few years ago when the average attendance was down to three," Henry Peasgood replied. "The same three eighty-six year old ladies every time. It got to the stage where the vicar asked them what hymns they wanted before the service started. Until one of them asked for *See Amid The Winter's Snow*. In July."

We agreed, on balance, that this new hymn book wasn't such a good idea.

The conversation then moved to the choir summer party at Cora's house on the evening of 27th July. This promises to be the choir social event of the year, with not only choir members but family and friends as well. The evening starts with a strawberry tea, and this is then followed by the first half of the entertainment, consisting of unaccompanied part-songs and madrigals outside. We then adjourn indoors for the food and conversation, although if the weather is warm we may wish to go back outside into the garden. The evening finishes with everyone being invited to perform their individual party pieces.

I nobly volunteered to help make up the madrigal group, hoping this would let me off having to offer something towards the end of the evening, but far from it. I had hoped that if pressed I could just do a couple of G & S numbers but Hazel seemed to think I might like to do a monologue entitled *The Green Eye On The Little Yellow God.* Everyone else agreed I should definitely do it, implying it was the most brilliant piece ever written by anyone on any subject. Not that anyone seems to have a copy of it.

Still, even that can't be as bad as Queenie Haverthwaite's proposed Abba medley. Or *No-One Loves A Fairy When She's Forty.* Sung by Arthur Ramsbottom.

Sunday 30th June – *FIFTH SUNDAY AFTER TRINITY*

Lesley asked us if we'd all say a little prayer for Jane, who leaves at lunchtime for France. She then came up to me brandishing a card and asking if I could organise all the choir members to sign it before they left this morning. Not sure what part of "rubbing," "my," "nose," "in" and "it" she didn't understand.

Being Petertide, we sang Durufle's powerful *Tu Es Petrus* this morning. Singing in Latin is always a bit of a challenge and might be seen by some to be a bit anachronistic but as Tripplehorn philosophically pointed out "It's a lovely language to sing in, and your diction is so bad the congregation probably think you're singing in Latin every Sunday." The vicar mentioned that Mike Stamford had been ordained in London yesterday. Mike was a choirboy at St Basil's from the age of ten up until the day he left for university – a bit like Jane, I suppose. Stories about his exploits in the choir abound – the most famous, or infamous, being his pouring treacle into the organ pipes after being told off by the then choirmaster Mr Phineas Meade-Ratchett for audibly sucking a sweet during the two minutes' silence on Remembrance Sunday. I'm not sure the organ ever quite recovered. Or Mr Phineas Meade-Ratchett.

JULY

Tuesday 2nd July

To the library at lunchtime to see if a copy of the monologue was available. Unfortunately I had had a particularly stressful morning in the office and simply could not remember the title. Moreover I had neither the patience or the resources to telephone round the choir. I told the librarian that it was quite a long title and I knew the word "yellow" came into it. She said nothing immediately came to mind but she would mull over it during the afternoon and let me know what she came up with.

Much later I was interrupted in the middle of quite a difficult report I was writing to be told that the library had located exactly what it was I was looking for. Decided to abandon any more work for today and dashed round to the library, catching them seconds before they shut. To be presented with a copy of *Tie A Yellow Ribbon Round The Old Oak Tree*.

The agenda for tonight's PCC meeting was formidable and after such a frustrating day I simply could not face sitting up until gone midnight discussing the funding for new hedge strimmers and the replacement of the arthritic Mrs Oxtoby as head of the church hall cleaning team. Somewhat boldly, I asked if the one agenda item I really needed to contribute to – the adoption of the new hymn book – could be brought up from item 21 to item 4, immediately after Matters Arising, so I could get off and have an early night. Amazingly, the chairman readily agreed, and I had barely started reading my guide book on the conquest of Kilimanjaro, which I had brought with me to while away the first three items, before the item was called on. I felt I put forward the choir's case very well: that the existing books had several years' worth of life left in them, the congregation were comfortable with them, and there were insufficient good hymns in the new books that weren't in the existing ones. The vicar responded by saying that that was a matter of opinion, to wit Frank Tripplehorn's opinion, and that if we were to move forward as a church community we needed to shift away from what was comfortable and samey and should try more challenging hymnody that jerked us out of our cosy complacency and made us think about where we were going as Christians. There were a number of rather sycophantic murmurs of approval of these sentiments, but I found an unlikely ally in Sidney Plumtree who said he found the hymns we sang never failed to challenge and inspire him, and to imply we sang them mechanically and unfeelingly was, with great respect, the grossest insult to our intelligence. He reminded us that many of the St Basil's congregation had defected from the town's Methodist Church when the elders there had forsaken hymn books for overhead projectors and the organ for electronic keyboard and guitar. His comments were also greeted with sage nodding of heads, not least from the ageing Percy Applewhite, although it could be that he had just dropped off to sleep. Eventually it was agreed to put it to the vote. It was decided, by a single vote, that we should *not* introduce the new books.

I think I might ditch my plans to climb Kilimanjaro. Compared with winning a vote at a St Basil's PCC meeting, it could only be a sad anticlimax.

Wednesday 3rd July

Am now in possession of *The Green Eye On The Little Yellow God.*

Sidney Plumtree rang me this evening, principally to tell me I'd left my Kilimanjaro book at the PCC meeting in my anxiety to get away last night. "I'm afraid you lost the vote after all," he went on. "You may remember Percy Applewhite voted for you. We'd got to item 18 at just turned eleven when someone suddenly remembered his vote couldn't count."

"What, because he was asleep when he put his hand up?" I asked.

"No, because he's not actually on the PCC at all," Sidney replied. "He got voted off at the May meeting, but no-one realised it till it was too late. So we had another vote, and you were defeated by one. Shame you'd gone by then. Chairman said if it had been tied, he'd have used his casting vote by voting for you."

Tripplehorn will do his nut. If I ever summon up the strength to tell him.

Through gritted teeth, and having resolved to check the finer details of my life insurance policy, I ventured to suggest that anyone who attends a PCC meeting purely for the fun of it must be dangerously close to being sectioned.

"Oh, I don't know," said Sidney. "Compared with people whose idea of fun is scaling Killamangiro, it seems quite harmless to me."

He may change his opinion when I leave Percy Applewhite alone in a room for ten minutes with Frank Tripplehorn and his rusty tuning fork.

Friday 5th July

Quite an amazing turn of events today.

Was sitting in my office minding my own business when an e-mail came through from none other than Jane Markwick. I'd forgotten she had my e-mail address. Although she has quickly settled into her job as a waitress in St Pierre, a picturesque small town in the Dordogne, she'd felt a little lonely on her first afternoon so had gone to the town's church and got talking to Father Beranger, the priest there. When informed that she was a keen singer, he had told her that his church had a fine choir, but explained that they took most of

August off because of holidays. He had said it was "such a peetee" that when holidaymakers came down from "ze beeg ceetees" and packed the church during August, "zair is nobodee to seeng for zem." Jane had suggested that if some of his parishioners were prepared to help with accommodation, why didn't the St Basil's choir come over to St Pierre for a couple of Sundays and lead the worship. Their church can provide an organist if we can't. With Tripplehorn away, and the choir in consequent semi-idleness, she reckoned it was an ideal time to go.

My first instinct was that it was just too short notice, and that most people would have made plans for August already. I was also apprehensive over Tripplehorn's reaction to our doing something of this nature in his absence. But as I continued with the affairs of the day, I began to feel quite excited at the prospect. I've got some leave due to me in August and although I had tentatively planned a few days' walking in Cornwall I've no difficulty with changing my plans. By the end of the afternoon, in my mind's eye I was sitting on the plane, sipping a dry white wine and gazing down at the sundrenched rolling French fields.

By half past nine that night, however, I was sitting in a proverbial tailback on the M25 somewhere round junction eleven. Tripplehorn, while not opposed in principle to our going, said he couldn't see how we would cope with the language barrier as well as the musical demands, pointing out that most of the choir can't sing in English let alone in French. It was likely, he pointed out, to be intolerably hot; it was most improbable that church funds would stretch to subsidising it; he knew the town in question, a vastly overrated tourist trap without a decent beer to be had in the place; and his mother would exact terrible revenge if he even thought about cancelling their holiday together. One by one, the others made their excuses. Queenie Haverthwaite has a phobia about flying and boats, Gordon Hunnisett couldn't get time off work, Joan Trumpington's leg was due for draining, Cora Willoughby-Smith has never trusted the French since her grandfather was short-changed in a public toilet in Azay-le-Rideau, Hazel Ledworthy has a bowel condition which makes it inadvisable for her to sit in the same position for more than thirty-eight minutes and therefore could not endure a long plane or coach journey, Arthur Ramsbottom takes his aged aunt to Frinton-on-Sea every August, has done since 1967 and has no intention of stopping now, and Irving Cattermole said that if we thought we could entice him from the Test cricket and his Sunday papers in the garden to a strange church in a strange country where the only thing to sustain him through interminable services in incomprehensible language was a diet of frogs' legs and snails served up by a garlic-encrusted peasant with no more words of

English in his head than a Venusian dung-beetle, we had another think coming, thank you very much.

We adjourned to the pub afterwards, my dream in tatters. So it was to my complete surprise when Tripplehorn came over to us, sat down with his gin and tonic, made himself comfortable and said "Well, now we've got all those no-hopers out of our hair....let's do it!"

I nearly fell out of my seat. "You...you mean go to the Dordogne?" I spluttered.

"That's right," said Tripplehorn. "There are enough of us. Just."

"Us?" Rachel echoed.

"That's right," he said. "I'll come with you. I'll palm my mum off on to my brother. Lovely area of France. Quite comfortable out of the sun. We'll squeeze some cash out of the treasurer, call it mission work. If their organist's available I can bolster up the basses. Great little town. Some of the best booze in the country, as well. If you know where to look for it."

It's so nice to have a choirmaster who knows his own mind.

I'd never seen him in such excellent humour. He even said he was looking forward to getting to work on my Harvest anthem in September with a view to it being performed at the big Harvest service at the end of that month. Having had a couple of sleepless nights worrying about the hymn book vote, I realised this was the perfect moment to break it to him, and did so. "Oh, don't worry," he said. "The vicar told me on Wednesday morning. I knew we'd be stuck with it in the end. Quite a decent hymn book, actually. And Lesley's right. The pages certainly do smell very nice."

Sunday 7ᵗʰ July – *SIXTH SUNDAY AFTER TRINITY*

Tripplehorn was beaming from ear to ear this morning. Yesterday, following some lengthy telephone conversations, we'd managed to firm up all the arrangements for the St Pierre trip, agreeing that we would travel out by coach and ferry on the night of Friday 16ᵗʰ/ Saturday 17ᵗʰ August and return on Bank Holiday Monday, 26ᵗʰ August. Jane will sort out all the accommodation from her end with Father Beranger. Tripplehorn has managed to wangle a substantial sum of money out of the treasurer to cover most of the travel costs, claiming our journey to be part of St Basil's overseas mission. He really has got a nerve.

Not only was he excited about our French trip but he was also chuckling to one of the sidesmen about the composition of the choir that are left behind to lead the St Basil's worship on the two Sundays we're away. He now claims to be looking forward to the new hymn books, has even agreed that they are to be introduced from 15ᵗʰ September, seemed unusually happy to let Cora murder the solo in Vaughan Williams' *O Taste And See* this morning, and even laughed off the failure of a good half of us to repeat the second part of the psalm chant at verse 11 of psalm 94 instead of verse 23. Yet I am sure it was he who once made the memorable comment that "there are no choirs in heaven, they're all in hell getting their psalms right."

Wednesday 10th July

Because of the amount of work involved in planning and rehearsing for our French trip, and the need to rehearse madrigals for the party on the 27th, it had been agreed that we would have two extra choir meetings this month, tonight and next Wednesday. Alison entertained us tonight. It was a beautiful evening so we sat in their garden, looking out towards acres of unspoilt countryside.

We've agreed that we will sing two services on each Sunday – mass according to their liturgy, and then an evensong in English according to the *Book Of Common Prayer*. We will also do a concert during the week using some of our party pieces.

Since Sunday, Eileen Crosby has had to pull out, so our group will consist of Alison and her children, Lesley, Jane, Margaret, Rachel, Craig, Brian, Henry and myself. In order to boost the numbers a little, Tripplehorn has enlisted the services of three outside singers, none of whom were present tonight: Samantha Ashton, whose talents had been so rudely brushed aside by Cora and her coven in early March, Julie Bukowski from Tripplehorn's adult education class, and an older man, a friend of Tripplehorn's from up North, rejoicing in the name of Charles Tyrebuck.

Our boat leaves during the afternoon of the 16th, and we then travel overnight by coach to our destination. It thus promises to be an interesting Saturday, with accommodation being sorted out and a rehearsal which Tripplehorn insists we have before going in to sing on the Sunday. "I hope Mr Tyrepump will stand the pace," Alison observed. "It's Buck," Tripplehorn corrected her. "Buck Tyrepump, then," Matthew rejoined.

The prospect of spending half the night in a coach with him is too hideous to contemplate.

We then went on to discuss accommodation. "I understand we're being put up by the locals," said Henry. "That's right," said Tripplehorn. "I see it as very much an integral part of the experience – that we reach out to a community in another part of our world with the gifts our Lord has instilled in us, testifying to our Christian brothers and sisters across the boundaries of sea and culture, and through sharing in the lives, the hopes and the fears of those receiving us into our homes, deepen our understanding of the social infrastructure of God's earthly kingdom."

"And what if there aren't enough families to have us?" Henry enquired.

"Do what I intend to do," said Tripplehorn, "and book in at the hotel."

Friday 12th July

Arrived at choir a little late tonight to find everyone waiting outside the church with no sign of Tripplehorn or Joan Trumpington, the only ones with keys.

To begin with, the conversation was quite lively, and Matthew told me a couple of jokes he'd heard at school that day which were surprisingly new and surprisingly clean. But as the minutes ticked by everybody began to get increasingly impatient. It was left to a few hardy souls to try and lift the mood of the party.

"Something like this happened at a youth convention I went to with my brother," said Margaret Pardew. "There were about forty of us and we were all wanting to get into this building that we were preparing for a big praise and worship outreach event. There was only one door and it was locked. It wouldn't budge at all. We were told the caretaker was out and nobody knew who else might have a key. Anyway, we decided we'd sing some of our worship songs. And as we sang to the Lord, suddenly this stranger came out of nowhere, came up to the door, pushed it, and it opened. Just like that. Then he turned round and disappeared. We'd not seen him before and we've not seen him since. A small, mysterious-looking man with a ring in one ear and small tufts of hair on an otherwise bald head. The caretaker arrived at the end of the evening and said the door was impossible to open without a key and he had the only set. It was the best youth convention ever. And but for this stranger it would never have happened."

"I remember about forty of us waiting to get into a church once," said Irving Cattermole. "It was for a big concert and we were the choir. There was only one door and it was locked. No key, no nothing. Anyway we decided to sing. And suddenly this stranger came out of nowhere, right up to us. Never seen him before or since. A great tall beetle-browed man with a scar on his forehead." "And he pushed open the door too?" Matthew asked in amazement. "No," said Irving Cattermole. "He told us to shut up because he couldn't concentrate on *Fifteen To One.*"

A few moments later a young man arrived, in open neck shirt and shorts. "Sorry to have kept you," he said. "Mike Pitheavlis. Frank's had a bad hayfever attack and asked me to take choir tonight. Thought you started at eight."

Fortunately he had a key and moments later we were rattling through Sunday's music. It was clear he had no intention of prolonging proceedings any longer than he had to, with liberal use of such expressions as "It'll come out in the wash" and "Just go over that in your heads before Sunday" whenever we hit a wrong note. At twenty to nine he sprang up from the organ seat, said "I'm off for a swim," and moments later he was gone.

As we sat in the beer garden of the Holly Tree, I asked Rachel who Mike Pitheavlis was. "He's a brilliant organist," she said, "but doesn't like church music. And I don't think he'll be welcome back at St Basil's for a while. Not after the choice of voluntary he played for the service to mark the climax of the Week Of Celebration of Cultural Diversity and Prayer For Racial Awareness And Sensitivity."

"Which was?" I enquired.

"*The Golliwog's Cake Walk*," said Rachel.

Sunday 14th July – *SEVENTH SUNDAY AFTER TRINITY*

A beautiful sunny day, a good congregation boosted by a large crowd of visitors, and Tripplehorn in excellent humour. We sang as well as I can remember, although the anthem, *I Waited Patiently For The Lord* by a certain J.M. Bilslack, was dire. I really don't know where Tripplehorn drags these pieces from.

Margaret collared me afterwards and asked if I, along with some others from the choir, would sing at a friend's wedding in a big evangelical church in the Midlands on 3rd August. Two or three of their choir, or "worship group," as she called it, will be away. I said jokingly in the hearing of Lesley Markwick, "I don't know if I can, but I'm sure Lesley would love to come along." Lesley's hatred of the "happy clappy" brigade is legendary in the choir so I was moderately embarrassed when Margaret immediately pounced upon her like a hawk upon its prey, and tried to convince her of the joys of a hot summer Saturday shaking tambourines in the industrial suburbs of Birmingham. She'd have had an easier ride cold-calling would-be purchasers of timeshare apartments in Kosovo.

Arrived at one thirty for the barbecue. Mike Pitheavlis was there, having been invited along as a token of thanks for helping us out on Friday night, and he introduced me to his very attractive sister Karen who's staying with him for the weekend. I was delighted that my choir membership had resulted in my meeting another such attractive girl, and in view of the uncertain state of my relationship with Jane, had no compunction about spending most of the afternoon talking with her and getting to know her. It was a glorious afternoon and although Brian had problems in getting the barbecue going and as a result the food wasn't great, I couldn't have cared less. Karen is back in the area on Friday week, has agreed to meet me for a drink after rehearsal that night, and said she'd come to the choir party the following night. Before we knew it, it was six o'clock. I had a few bits of work I needed to prepare for a meeting tomorrow, and as Karen was also making noises about going, I decided this would be a good time to leave myself. I went across to say goodbye to Rachel, and found her and Lesley tucking into appetising-looking pizzas, chatting to a middle-aged man with bushy eyebrows and striped bow tie. He looked like a cross between a university professor and a circus clown. "Tell me," Lesley said, after I'd thanked Rachel for inviting me, "What did you think of the anthem this morning?"

"To be honest," I replied, my tongue loosened by my enjoyable and somewhat liquid afternoon, "I thought it was total garbage. A piece of sentimental claptrap that would have sent even the Waltons scurrying for their sickbags."

Whereupon Lesley, without warning, virtually frogmarched me round the side of the house and out into the street. "Did you not know who that man was?" she screeched, when safely out of earshot. "That was John Bilslack, who wrote that anthem that you just rubbished!"

Decided that returning to bid my farewell to Karen was not the best move in the circumstances and made my exit with all the confidence and self-assurance of a Safeway raspberry jelly.

Tripplehorn phoned me much later to ask if I was still okay to join the madrigal group for the summer party, and if I was all right for the rehearsal on Wednesday. In an effort to unburden myself following my latest *faux pas,* which had worried me sick all evening, I said to him "You remember that anthem we sang this morning?" "Oh, heavens, yes," he said. "Ghastly, wasn't it? I only did it because this year's the centenary of Bilslack's death." "But he was at the barbecue this afternoon," I replied. "I think you'll find he'd have been more likely to be *on* it," Tripplehorn chuckled.

Lost no time in phoning Lesley. "That'll teach you to try and get me to give up a perfectly decent Saturday for a crowd of light-bulb changers," she said. I couldn't resist asking whether their male companion, about whom I had been feeling seriously guilty for the past three and a half hours, was a musician of any description.

"I doubt it," she said. "He was the pizza delivery driver."

Wednesday 17th July

A glorious day: sunny, clear and not too hot. Inkbarrow Hill would have been a lovely place to spend a leisurely evening, but duty called, in the form of a madrigal rehearsal coupled with a planning meeting for the holiday. We've decided on eight madrigals in all, and sang them all through two or three times. Although Tripplehorn was rather fussier than might have been expected considering it's really only for fun, it should enhance the quality of the end product.

Spent some time during the planning meeting agreeing the selection of music. We all agreed it would be nice to sing something in French.

"There's always the German breakfast order," observed Henry Peasgood, "better known as the *Cantique De Jean Racine*, by Gabriel Faure."

"What do you mean, German breakfast order?" Rachel inquired.

"The first line of the piece, Verbe egale. Vier bagel. Four bagels," Henry responded.

"I'm sorry, you've lost me," said Alison, expressing the sentiments of just about everyone.

"Except, of course, that if a German was ordering breakfast in England, he would speak in English," said Craig Dumbleton. "So he wouldn't ask for 'Vier bagel.' He'd ask for four bagels. And if he was ordering them in Germany, he wouldn't call them bagels. There'd be a German name for them."

"Not necessarily," said Henry Peasgood. "Bagels are bagels. It's like spaghetti. That's an Italian word, but everyone uses it when they mean spaghetti."

"I'm not even sure you can get bagels in Germany," said Lesley. "Mind you, I had some very good croissants in Utrecht once."

"Which happens to be in the Netherlands," said Craig Dumbleton.

"Can I just get this right?" said Lesley. "You're suggesting we do a piece by Faure about a German bagel-maker by the name of Jean Racine putting in an order in English for spaghetti and croissants in the Netherlands."

"Let's just stick to *Frere Jacques*, then," said Tripplehorn.

Friday 19th July

My birthday. A nice post, including cards from Margaret, Brian and Rachel, and Lesley. Jane e-mailed me a birthday greeting and said a card was on its way.

As my birthday fell on a choir night, I decided to splash out on a celebration iced rich fruit cake from the bakery near the office to have with our coffee tonight. Unfortunately we were very depleted at the rehearsal. To my great

103

disappointment Brian and Rachel had gone away for the weekend, Alison announced her children were sick and she would need to leave as soon as the practice was over, Lesley had a streaming cold and left halfway through, Craig simply did not appear but was thought by Tripplehorn to be at the Train Spotters Ball, Eileen Crosby and Arthur Ramsbottom were on holiday, Hazel Ledworthy, Gordon Hunnisett and Irving Cattermole disappeared promptly as they always do, and Tripplehorn had some "sorting out" to do in the vestry. This just left Cora, Queenie, Henry, Margaret and myself, and of these, Henry being diabetic couldn't touch my cake, Queenie being on a diet said she didn't feel she could either, and Cora pronounced herself to be suffering from a nut allergy which precluded her from tasting it. Only Margaret helped herself to a slice. Suspecting that she had done so out of sympathy rather than because of hunger or a sweet tooth – I know her to have the appetite of a sparrow – I felt it only right to repay her selflessness by asking her to share a birthday drink with me at the Holly Tree.

It was a very sultry still evening, the place was packed, and we were quite fortunate to find a free table in the pub garden. As soon as we did sit down, however, Margaret lost little time in updating me with her latest litany of misfortunes. In the last week Trixie, her beloved but dilapidated Fiat Panda, had been pronounced by her mechanic to be terminally ill and beyond repair, her cat had died, her mother had had a severe asthma attack, and her brother had had to pull out of an important Christian youth event because of a bad back which had also kept him off work for most of the last fortnight. "Now tell me the bad news," I said jokingly, hoping that she would appreciate my attempt at humouring her. But I might as well have been trying to humour a plum duff. In answer to my question, she replied that the bad news was that nobody from St Basil's choir was able to commit themselves to supplementing the worship group on 3rd August in Birmingham. She told me the church where the wedding was taking place, which two years previously was dead as a dodo, was now one of the fastest-growing churches in Britain, that Kevin and Sharon, the couple concerned, were family friends and were spearheading this revival, that she was hoping to forge musical links between them and St Basil's with this as the first step, and that the singer shortage was a severe body-blow to her plans to bring Birmingham back to God through music. In fact she went on as though it were the greatest calamity to befall the Christian Church in modern times. As I sipped at my lukewarm orange juice, I felt myself being sucked into submission as helplessly and impotently as a Pennine hiker caught in a peat bog during a flash flood, and finally capitulated, being rewarded with a huge hug and an embarrassingly wet kiss. For my next birthday, I think I'll join Craig

Dumbleton. Bopping the night away in an off-the-shoulder Parka on platform three at East Croydon.

Sunday 21st July – *EIGHTH SUNDAY AFTER TRINITY*

Tripplehorn announced that Friday's practice would be the last Friday practice till September. We can cover the music for the next two Sundays then, and he's away after that. A woefully small congregation this morning, so much so that the vicar changed one of the hymns to enable us to sing the line "Lord we are few, but thou art near." And with so many choir members away, Tripplehorn opted for a unison anthem from the easy section of the new anthem book. At least it wasn't by J.M. Bilslack.

As we were disrobing afterwards, Tripplehorn came in and asked if any of us wanted to "walk in the air for twenty-five quid." I assumed it was some form of sponsored hang-gliding event but it turned out that a couple are getting married in St Basil's in September and want *Walking In The Air*, from the animated film *The Snowman*, as a solo. The soloist has been promised this fairly generous cash gift on top of the normal choir wedding fee. "As the wretched thing's on every Christmas, I did suggest they got married on Christmas Day and just have the telly in the background," said Tripplehorn. He didn't sound as though he was joking.

I'd decided it was time to take the choir coffee urn home for descaling. As I was struggling up the path with that and a folder of music, Lord Buttermere came over to me and kindly offered to relieve me of the music. He only rarely comes to St Basil's but is well known as a musical connoisseur; he has given talks on Radio 3 on the music of Chopin, writes regular musical reviews for the papers, and in his time has played second violin in the LSO. He explained that he'd been at church this morning to discuss arrangements for his daughter's wedding, which promises to be a very lavish spectacle indeed, with a formidable array of fine music to which he was sure the choir would do full justice. I told him how much I was looking forward to it."Would you believe it," I laughed, as I loaded the urn into the car, "some couple want *Walking In The Air* for their wedding. Inappropriate or what! I suppose you have to expect anything of people who've never been near a church in their lives. But honestly. What planet are they on, for goodness sake?"

"Same as mine, I hope," replied Lord Buttermere, "seeing as it's my daughter who asked for it."

Friday 26th July

Decided I'd had enough of tripping over the wretched urn every time I walked along the landing to the bathroom, and I'd just made sufficient room for it in one of my kitchen cupboards at breakfast time when the phone went. It was Cora checking that I was bringing a sweet tomorrow night. As I returned to the kitchen, the urn suddenly took it upon itself to topple down out of the cupboard, bouncing off my right shoulder and careering into my bowlful of Bran Flakes. I had intended to get down to descaling tomorrow, but decided I could put it off no longer, filled the urn with water and descaler and switched it on. Nothing happened.

Fortunately, Mick Gorman's electrical goods and repair shop is just round the corner from my office and they promised they would fix it for me within a fortnight.

Was quite excited about the prospect of meeting Karen for a drink tonight and then going with her to the party tomorrow. Today's post brought the running order for the items that will form the party entertainment, and it was with mixed feelings that I noted that my monologue is second from last. On the debit side, I will be sitting it out rather than getting it over with, and I have no chance of making a speedy exit with Karen if Arthur Ramsbottom's oh-so-convincing forty-year-old fairy, or Joan Trumpington's music hall medley liberally laced with invitations to "have a banana," get too much. On the other hand, there's always the chance that by the time I do get on everyone will be so bored or so tired that it really wouldn't matter two hoots if I stood up there and recited the 1965 Ministry of Agriculture directive on the movement of linseed oil.

Karen arrived in church just as we were finishing our rehearsal. It was a pity that she should approach the choir stalls, clad in a very short dress and very high heels, just as Cora, embroiled in the catering arrangements for the party, turned to me and said "You did say you were bringing a tart tomorrow night, didn't you." And trying to explain what she meant afterwards only made it worse.

Saturday 27th July

Writing after the choir party, I would now like to conduct my own award ceremony.

Best moment: Henry Peasgood being asked by a friend of Lesley Markwick to give his considered opinion on the vintage and country of an origin of a drink given to him, offering the opinion that it was 1980 vintage of Rhenish origin with just a daring hint of Mosel, to be told it was in fact a mixture of

Tesco's sparkling grape juice, KwikMart's own brand Economy lemonade, and two measures of Lesley's home-made balsamic vinegar.

Most unconvincing performance: Arthur Ramsbottom who might have got away with his fairy costume had the ensemble not been finished off by a pair of paisley-pattern ankle socks and smelly thirty-year-old Adidas trainers.

Worst performance: Joan Trumpington whose music hall medley was so full of wrong notes and forgotten segments that none of us, least of all her, knew if we were watching the bang of the poor but honest farmer's gun inside the Old Bull and Bush, dilly-dallying on the way to the Siegfried Line with a lovely bunch of coconuts, or having a banana on the Lambeth Walk in our cor-blimey trousers.

Most discerning audience: Zoe and her friend Katie, who the minute Cora opened her mouth to sing her *Carmen* compilation hurried to the next room announcing that *Casualty* was just about to start on BBC1.

Most ill-advised performance: Queenie, Hazel, Craig and Henry, whose spoof psalm chant of the exclusion clauses in relation to a policy of pleasure-boat insurance might have worked better had they confined themselves to the first dozen clauses rather than all fifty-nine.

Most contrived critique: Tripplehorn who after we struggled, in intense heat, to execute our madrigals in front of an audience that was too busy drinking tea and guzzling strawberries to pay the slightest attention to what we were singing, remarking that he had heard pleasanter sounds when his niece emptied a cup of boiling hot coffee over his *Best Of Val Doonican* LP which his brother happened to be playing at the time.

Most unpleasant surprise: Helping myself to a tasty-looking slice of cooked meat and wolfing it down, to be informed by Queenie that she was delighted that at least someone had been brave enough to try her sauted pig's livers.

Most damning comment: Hazel Ledworthy who after I had given, I felt, an entertaining rendition of the monologue in suitable costume, earning enthusiastic applause from the adults and enthusiastic snores from the children, sniffed and said "It has been traditional to recite the piece from memory" before marching off into the kitchen, giving me a look as icy as the strawberry Cornettos lying in the freezer compartment of Mario's North Pole Snack Bar.

Best display of insensitivity: Craig Dumbleton, seconds after I had watched Karen, together with my renewed hopes of a relationship based on choir membership, disappearing into the night in her boyfriend's bright blue 1985 Ford Escort, asking if I had had the chance to visit the newly-refurbished railway station left-luggage office at Raynes Park.

Sunday 28th July – *NINTH SUNDAY AFTER TRINITY*

We have a problem. Cora Willoughby-Smith has always refused to sit next to Queenie Haverthwaite, making no secret of the fact that not only does she take up far too much space on the ledges but her voice has no blendability whatsoever. Now it seems she has no wish to sing adjacent to Joan Trumpington, following a contretemps last night over a plate of vol-au-vents. This means that she has no choice but to sit next to Hazel Ledworthy. Which presents another problem – to wit, Hazel Ledworthy has always stedfastly refused to sit anywhere near Cora Willoughby-Smith.

It may just be coincidence that the vicar, whose last service it is with us until September, preached about the vital importance of maintaining a united Christian brotherhood and setting aside the petty differences that divide us. The vicar regards this as essential if we are to reach out successfully to the not-yet-converted of our parish. But if the antics of C.W.S. and H.L. after the service are markers of our progress in this regard, they will have to stay not-yet-converted for a while longer.

Margaret asked me if I wanted a lift to Birmingham on Saturday, in her brother's car, and offered me a room in the friend's house she's staying overnight in after the reception. When I told her I would prefer to make my own way there and back she seemed quite upset. I'm still hoping I can get out of it altogether but goodness knows how, especially as I seem now to be the only other choir member that is going along and forging this supposedly vital musical link between the music-making fraternities of the two churches.

As we were leaving, Cora Willoughby-Smith was still very upset and talking about resignation. After she'd gone, I told Lesley I imagined Tripplehorn would be pleased. "I don't think so," she said. "If she goes, we'll get Davina Prendergast back. She only left because of Cora."

"Is she that bad?" I asked.

"She's caused at least five choir members to resign," she said. "And Billy Moffat's never recovered since the time she boxed his ears one Sunday after mattins."

"A mischievous boy soprano, then, was he?" I enquired.

"Not quite," said Lesley. "He's actually the Rural Dean."

AUGUST

Saturday 3rd August

Having resigned myself to going up to Birmingham today, decided to set out at seven thirty to avoid the worst of the traffic, and I was on the point of leaving the house when the phone rang. It was Lesley saying that Jane had been on the phone at dead of night last night asking if I'd received my e-mail from her at the office, and really concerned in case I hadn't. Decided to make a detour to the office to look at it. Damnably, there was no response from my PC at all, and when I phoned the help desk I was told the network was out of action until eight thirty for essential maintenance work. Rang Lesley from the office to find out what Jane wanted. She merely answered "It is rather personal." When I did manage to download the message, at twenty to nine, I could see what she meant. Basically, Jane is really missing me and wants to know if I still feel about her as I did. I e-mailed her straight back replying that my feelings for her are even stronger now, then logged off and shot off.

But the result was that I left a good hour and a half later than expected, and got caught in three huge tailbacks en route. It was a humid, close morning and I was sweltering in my car. By a miracle, however, I located the Church of Christ Triumphant in Garrett Street very easily and rushed in to find that although the rehearsal had begun I was only about twenty minutes late. Didn't even look out for Margaret, but quickly ascertained from one of the singers where the tenors were, was handed a file of music, and took my place at the end of the third row. Was slightly nonplussed by the selection, all of it on the themes of judgment, heaven and hell, and all in gospel style, but that was the happy couple's privilege. I kept trying to make out Margaret but I just couldn't see her at all. Maybe she had got stuck in even worse traffic than I'd had. Not at all surprised that there were so few white singers; Margaret had mentioned that the church contained a very large African element in its congregation, including the conductor. He could have taught Tripplehorn a thing or two, I reflected. He was demanding and uncompromising, but had a lovely smile and a real sense of humour. It was just a pity that we had to sing through the songs so many times, often to perfect the tiniest technical detail. Even though the quality of sound was tremendous, there is a limit to how many times one can bear to repeat a single line of music, especially to the words "They will go to eternal damnation." Hardly the ideal send-off for a newly-married couple, either.

The wedding was due to start at two thirty but by five past two we were still rehearsing and no guests appeared to be arriving at all. I said to the man on my left "The wedding is soon, isn't it?" "Oh yes, brother, very soon," he replied. "I mean, nobody seems to be getting ready or anything," I persisted. "We are all ready here, my friend," he answered. "Ready for the glorious feast at which the Lamb of God becomes wedded to his Holy Church." I told him my immediate concern was the wedding of Kevin Smith and Sharon Crump. "I don't know about that," he replied. "We are members of the West Midland Adventist Gospel Chorale rehearsing for a concert in the city tonight." Reached in my pocket for the particulars which Margaret had given me, and to my horror I saw that I'd come to the wrong church altogether and I should have been somewhere else. To be precise, the Church of Christ The King, Barrett Street.

Fortunately my companion couldn't have been nicer, telling me that lots of people made the same mistake and that "our dear brothers at Christ the King are only ten minutes away." Which was just as well, with the wedding due to start in twelve and a half. "Turn right into St Wilfrid's Road," he went on. "Left into Carpenter Street, left again into St Asaph Road, second right into Lozell Parade, fourth left into Mungrove Park, second right into Barratt Street. Just after the temporary traffic lights. And watch out along Mungrove Park. Today's the St Ignatius School Community Carnival and Centenary Pageant."

Despite my companion's time estimate, I actually reached the church just as the happy couple were emerging from it as man and wife. The crowds surrounding them were colossal and it took me a further five minutes to force my way through the melee to find Margaret. I half hoped she would jump down my throat, thereby giving me an excuse to beat a hasty retreat and make it home in time for *Who Wants To Be A Millionaire*, but she was maddeningly forgiving, telling me she quite understood, and she looked forward to my accompanying her to the reception which was due to begin in twenty minutes. I couldn't think of anything worse, but my defences were shattered. Fortunately the reception was at the scout hut just over the road, so there was no more driving to do, but it was still the longest two and a half hours of my life, consisting of a rather nasty stand-up finger buffet in the company of a group of total strangers in a room so crowded that one could hardly lift an arm to manoeuvre food into one's mouth, let alone move around. Margaret, to her credit, did her best to introduce me to a few of the crowd, but it was virtually impossible to hear or to be heard, so that I had no idea whether the guest I was talking to at any one time was a missionary spreading God's word in the slums of Sao Paolo or a telesalesman annoying the natives of Droitwich every evening with offers of cutprice life insurance and inferior double glazing.

111

Relief came in the form of the departure of some of the guests at just gone five thirty, which gave us all a little more room to breathe, and some short but amusing speeches from the stage. Then, however, the best man announced "a special treat for the bride and groom and their guests." He went on "They're singing live in the centre of Birmingham tonight but they've dropped in specially for a warm-up to entertain us all.....The West Midland Adventist Gospel Chorale!" Suddenly the curtains behind him parted to reveal the same singers and conductor I'd been singing with a few hours ago, and within seconds they had launched into one of the songs I'd been rehearsing earlier at such painful length. Unable to stomach it once again, I turned to Margaret and told her I had to go. Fortunately she didn't bother to argue, merely producing a large carrier bag containing my choir robe which she had needlessly brought all the way to Birmingham with her and which I'll need for church tomorrow.

Hurried back to the car determined to get away as soon as possible. Opened the passenger door, hurled the robe on the passenger seat, turned the lock in the passenger door, and shut it. Only to realise I'd chucked the car keys into the car with the robe and was now locked out.

I dare say a half-decent car thief could have got inside it in seconds, and it was unfortunate that I'd chosen an evening on which all the indigenous hot-wirers seemed to be operating elsewhere. Having decided waiting for roadside assistance would be about as fun as watching a fresh coat of paint dry on the wall of Willesden bus depot gents toilet, I could really have done with some expert criminal assistance in forcing my way in without recourse to my eventual method.

Staggered into my house four hours later and found a message on my answering machine from Lesley, to the effect that Jane was most upset I'd not e-mailed her back, and she was going out to drown her sorrows with a man named Francois. I just found enough strength to get round to the office to find that owing to a systems failure my reply this morning had never actually been sent.

Never mind. I may have lost Jane, upset Margaret, missed the very thing I made the long journey for, engaged in inaudible conversations over inedible food, and be facing a bill of several hundred pounds for a new drivers' door window and professional vacuuming of loose shards of glass from all over the front half of my car, not to mention possible prosecution for TWOCing if my break-in was caught on close-circuit television.

But at least I know I'll be welcomed back with open arms into the West Midland Adventist Gospel Chorale.

Sunday 4th August – *TENTH SUNDAY AFTER TRINITY*
Cora Willoughby-Smith was back this morning. It seems, however, that a condition of her remaining with us is that she has her own place and her own lectern, a discreet distance from Joan Trumpington. The vol-au-vent war is clearly far from over.

Tripplehorn was there for parish eucharist this morning but the vicar was away. So were most of the congregation. There were enough of us in the choir, however, for Tripplehorn to request the French party to stay on afterwards for an extra rehearsal for France, rather than attending on Wednesday as had been his original plan. He shoved a few pieces of music at us before the service and said "Look at these during the sermon, will you. It won't be worth listening to so you might as well make some use of the time." I saw Alison looking somewhat askance at his scathing comment, but it turned out to be absolutely right. The celebrant and preacher was a retired priest from Cornwall, Lawrence Doubtfire, who inflicted upon us one of the most rambling addresses I'd ever heard. He also seemed to be completely out of it during the second half of the service, forgetting to announce our anthem, *Lead Me Lord*, and then inserting it halfway through the eucharistic prayer. He also insisted on leaving the altar and coming down to join us to sing it. This is one of the easier pieces in our repertoire and well known to us all, and we might actually have produced quite a good performance had not our unexpected additional member sung so loudly and at the same time so badly out of tune.

"At least he made the effort," Alison said philosophically afterwards.

"Well, true," said Tripplehorn, "although it would have helped if he'd been singing *Lead Me Lord* rather than Elgar's *Ave Verum*. With his copy upside down."

Sunday 11th August – *ELEVENTH SUNDAY AFTER TRINITY*
As I lay in bed this morning, I looked back on a curious week with no singing or church-related activity of any kind. Quite missed our rehearsal on Friday evening. But with no vicar, no choirmaster and lots of regulars away this morning, felt no real enthusiasm for church. Was therefore pleasantly surprised to find a good contingent of visitors, Mike Pitheavlis unexpectedly at the organ, and Andy Bousfield, a former Sunday school teacher at St Basil's and one of the best preachers in the diocese, celebrating. Lesley, who I think took a bit of a shine to him, asked him what the subject of his sermon would be. "I'm going to talk about making more time for God," he answered. "Too many of us pack far too much into our lives. I want to stress the importance of slowing down the bustle and haste that so often dictates

113

our pattern of living and explore ways of letting God fill the spiritual void that is left by our stress and over-exertion." Mike overheard this and said rather too audibly "I hope he's quick about it. I need to be away by eleven." As if in anticipation of a lengthy homily, Mike did indeed play the opening hymns, psalm and Gloria at breakneck speed. Fortunately, perhaps, the address was of no more than average length and Mike did slow down later in the service, playing a beautiful voluntary in place of the anthem. Afterwards, Andy Bousfield said to Mike "That organ piece was perfect. Spiritually uplifting and inspiring, moving our hearts and minds to the plane where our Father would have us be. We are fortunate beings indeed that he instils in us the creative gifts to compose pieces of such beauty." Mike merely grinned and said "Oh, absolutely." As we were leaving I asked him who had in fact composed it. "No idea," he said. "I heard it on Japanese cable TV in the week. I think it was an advert for anti-dandruff shampoo."

Friday 16th August

Was just clearing my desk at the end of the morning, having booked the afternoon off, when the phone rang. It was Cora Willoughby-Smith reminding me that the urn still hasn't been returned from descaling and could I pop it back before going away as she and the non-attenders for France were rehearsing in church tonight with Arnold Petherbridge, the stand-in organist for Sunday's service, and they might want a drink afterwards. I'd quite forgotten the wretched thing, to be honest, but a quick phone call to Mick Gorman confirmed it was ready for us, and having left the office twenty minutes earlier than planned I was able to collect it and return it to the vestry.

We set off for France after lunch. I'm not sure what excited me more: the prospect of some really good singing in a beautiful part of France, or seeing Jane again. I've been reflecting all week that it shouldn't be too difficult to prise her away from the attentions of Francois and persuade her that the two of us are good together. It was that thought and that alone which enabled me to keep my sanity through an interminable coach trip to the ferry port along roads that were solid with holiday traffic and then a two hour delay before we could board our vessel owing to technical problems.

At least our three guests were all present and correct. Samantha Ashton has come along with her boyfriend Dave, and they spent most of the delay and the subsequent crossing entwined in each other. Julie Bukowski, on the other hand, very much on her own, spending much of the journey sitting reading a magazine. As it was such a hot night, her leather jeans might have been considered a surprising choice of clothing but certainly she caused a few eyes to turn, and but for Jane, I might well have been tempted to make a move on her myself. It was just a shame I should get off immediately on the wrong foot with my fellow tenor and introduce him to Lesley as Charles Tyremark. He didn't seem amused. Oh dear.

Saturday 17ᵗʰ August

We finally docked in France shortly after midnight, three hours late, with a twelve hour coach journey still to come. So weary were we that we slumped into our seats and it was only several hours later, in broad daylight, that I found myself stirring. It was a glorious sunny morning and the French countryside looked breathtakingly beautiful. I was really looking forward to getting to St Pierre, which according to the guidebook I'd borrowed from the library was a "historic unspoilt hilltop town, largely unaffected by the ravages of time, boasting many fine old buildings and surrounded by beautiful woodland with panoramic views to the nearby countryside." I turned to Lesley and said jovially "What a lovely morning to be meeting the love of my life again." She frowned and asked me who that was. "Jane, of course," I said. "That may be tricky," Lesley replied. "She's moved in with Francois and they're talking about getting married."

This was a huge blow, I don't mind admitting, and I was in pretty low spirits as we arrived in St Pierre, despite our having made up virtually all the time lost, and a very cordial welcome from our hosts in the town square. Jane was there, wearing the shortest shorts I think I'd ever seen, but I could barely bring myself to look at her. After a conference between Tripplehorn, who claims to be a fluent French speaker, and Father Beranger, it was agreed that having met our host families, freshened up and had a snack, we would meet back at the church at five for a full rehearsal for tomorrow, before a welcome meal that was being organised for us in the nearby church hall.

I was introduced to my host couple, Raoul and Mariette Ledunois, and within thirty seconds realised that their knowledge of English was non-existent. Fortunately French had been one of my A level subjects, and by trial and error we managed to get some sort of conversation going as we walked through the streets leading away from the square, and got into their car for the short drive to their house. Enjoyed a hot shower, a lie-down with yesterday's *Times* crossword, and a delicious slice of home-made cake with coffee. It certainly made up for the greasy burger and chips we'd had to endure at the café en route, brought up spectacularly by one of the party fifteen minutes after we'd got going again. No prizes for guessing who.

Tripplehorn looking remarkably pleased with himself as we reconvened for the rehearsal. I strongly suspect that not only is he in the Grand Hotel right on the square but, from a conversation I've overheard, St Basil's are indeed picking up the bill for it. It didn't take long, however, for him to lose his temper when we made an almighty hash of the responsorial psalm, and accuse us of having left our voices, not to mention our brains, somewhere in the English Channel. Charles Tyrebuck, who will be singing tenor together with Craig and me, rather cold, I thought. I guessed what was worrying him and said to him "I'm so sorry I got your name wrong." Instead of laughing it off, as I hoped he would, he replied simply "Good."

We adjourned straight from the rehearsal to the welcome meal, using a somewhat labyrinthine underground route from the church into the hall via the crypt. Places in the hall hadn't been allocated and having spurned the offer of a seat two places away from Jane, I saw a vacant seat right next to Julie who looked, if anything, even more stunning than she had last night. I had got as far as asking her if the seat was taken when a very large lady approached, literally shoved me aside and said "Zis is my place." By this time the only available seat was next to Charles Tyrebuck. With French speakers all around us, we had no choice but at least to try to get on and much to my relief, we did so, over a quite delicious four-course dinner. I was slightly surprised he should assume I knew so much about the internal administrative affairs of Ripon Cathedral, or indeed the church he attends in a town a few miles from there. But I was saved having my ignorance too starkly exposed because after the sweet course was served, an entertainment was provided for us. Father Beranger sang two beautiful French songs for us with accordion accompaniment, and then some of the host families very bravely led a music hall session, "to make you kind Eengleesh people feel at home." Their performance was certainly an improvement on Joan Trumpington's abject efforts of three weeks ago.

Although it was gone eleven by the time it finished, and none of us had been in bed for the last 36 hours, we were all in exuberant mood, buoyed up by the excellent wine that was provided with our meal. Raoul guessed, however, that I might be tired and anxious to be getting back, and headed for the door with Mariette. I saw Jane heading in my direction so deliberately turned away from her on the pretext of wanting to say goodnight to Charles, delighted that my earlier gaffe was now happily forgiven. As I did so, a very Gallic-looking old gentleman staggered tipsily up to us, his left arm draped round an equally merry Lesley Markwick, and, slapping Charles on the back with his right hand, he cried "How do you get zees strange name – how you say – Tyre Pump!" before exploding into a loud guffaw.

I was out of the hall and into Raoul's car before you could say "Oh Monsieur Porteur."

Sunday 18th August – *TWELFTH SUNDAY AFTER TRINITY*

Slept like a log and it was a real effort to get up this morning. Breakfast was a comparatively brief affair – a cup of coffee and a roll – then Raoul offered me a lift in for the nine o'clock rehearsal for the 10am mass. Was slightly surprised that Raoul should feel the need to leave at quarter past eight for the three-mile drive, and I was wondering if the Sunday morning rush-hour was particularly acute in St Pierre. It was only when we got there that he was able to explain, with all the sign language he could muster, that he thought I'd told him we were rehearsing at half past eight. So much for my A level French.

Decided to use the extra half-hour profitably and go for a wander round the town. It was a pity that I had no street plan with me, doubly so when I was quite unable to find my way back to the church and finally crept in at twenty past nine. Tripplehorn, of course, had to stop the rehearsal while I installed myself and found my place in the mass booklet, before asking me "Bit too much Chardonnay last night, then, eh?" Trust Lesley to start sniggering.

A big congregation – about five times as many as St Basil's would have seen this morning, I reckoned – and a nice welcome, in English, from Father Beranger before the service got under way. Unfortunately, Tripplehorn's command of French was not so great as to prevent him bringing us in for the Sanctus before the Eucharistic Prayer had even begun, or for the Great Amen before it had actually finished, or for the communion motet before the congregation had been invited to come up for communion. Then to make matters worse, his instruction to the organist that there was a cut in the middle of the motet was not heard or understood, leaving the poor organist thirty bars behind and panicked into a temporary pit stop. To give him credit, he'd almost caught us up as we were reaching the chequered flag.

We had four hours of free time before our 3.30 rehearsal for evensong. As we were leaving church, Jane came up to me, handed me a business card and told me "That's where I work. I'm working for the next couple of hours but should be free by two so come and meet me at work if you can." I coldly told her I'd think about it, and walked smartly away.

I enjoyed a pleasant stroll, alone, round the town, and found a seat at a pavement café out of the sun to enjoy a couple of chapters of my novel over a ham-filled baguette and a pint of beer. I was just finishing my baguette and wondering whether to meet Jane, when Margaret Pardew came hurrying up to me, insisted on joining me, and for the next two hours I listened while she revealed to me the latest ailments affecting every one of her family, from the depression afflicting her sister-in-law to the mange that's just been found on her cousin's albino rabbit. My gentle hints that time was marching on and

117

that we ought to be getting back to join the others did not stem the flow of gloom in the least, and to my embarrassment, I arrived back at church with Margaret to find I was late again, and the rehearsal was already in progress. As we made our way up the aisle to take our places, Father Beranger came up to us and kindly asked how we were settling in. He said he was a little concerned about tonight's evensong attendance because of "ze....I zink you say cleefhenger on ze box." As a cryptic crossword clue there was a certain something lacking, but eventually we established that the service clashed with the cliffhanging, or even cleefhenging, denouement of a serial drama on French TV which was being avidly followed by over half the population, Including, it seemed, Raoul and Mariette who I was told would not now be coming to the service but would meet me afterwards.

When we did eventually join the ranks, we felt we should tell Tripplehorn and ask him what he wanted to do. He looked accusingly at Margaret and said "You're the one who says it's God we sing to and we shouldn't worry who else is there."

However, even he was beginning to waver when after two and a half hours' bad-tempered rehearsing, Faure's *Cantique De Jean Racine* sounding worse than when we'd first sightread it, and Psalm 94 frankly hateful, the appointed time for the service arrived with nobody present whatsoever save Father Beranger – who couldn't very well have stayed away as he was taking it. Tripplehorn turned to us and said "If nobody comes in within the next thirty seconds I think we'll call it a night."

At that moment the door opened to admit a very elderly nun who genuflected, signed herself with the cross, and took a seat at the very back of the church. The fact that we had a congregation obliged us, in Tripplehorn's view, to proceed, and proceed we did. By a miracle, despite feeling hot and tired, we acquitted ourselves extremely well, and as we sang those poignant words of Psalm 94 – "For the Lord will not fail his people, neither will he forsake his inheritance" – I felt pleased and humbled that through the medium of music we were reaching out to another Christian sister in love despite the barriers of language and of culture. At the end of the service, we saw her get up, sign herself again, and leave in silence and dignity to face the rigours of the world once more, hopefully enriched by our offering of thanks and praise to God.

Father Beranger was all smiles afterwards. "So good of you to seeng this evening," he said to us. "I am sure zet God heard, though no-one else did." Tripplehorn turned to him and said "What about that nun?" "Ah," said Father Beranger. "She has heard nuzzing zeens nineteen seventy two. She is....how you put it....deaf as ze post box!"

118

Monday 19th August

Again slept very well and, with no singing today, enjoyed a very welcome lie-in. Yesterday evening's events had certainly taken their toll. Raoul gave me a lift into town just before midday and it was then my intention to see if Julie was around and suggest going for a coffee together, but there was no sign of her or indeed any other choir members. I spent some time in the tourist information office from which I gathered that there was a bus to the village of St Etienne de la Colline, described as one of the jewels of the surrounding area, in half an hour, and there was a bus back from there to St Pierre in the late afternoon. I decided to make the trip. The journey used up a good proportion of my available euros, and a pleasant late lunch in the village restaurant, La Bonne Creperie, accounted for almost all of the rest of them, but it was certainly worth the expenditure to enjoy provincial France at its best.

The bus got me back to St Pierre at twenty to six. Almost immediately I got off, I saw Alison and her children queuing for ice cream from the van parked in the square. "Oh, there you are," said Alison. "You missed a great day out." "Day out?" I queried. "Oh yes," she said. "One of the hosts took us all out in his minibus." I told her I knew nothing about it. "Well, it was advertised before both yesterday's rehearsals," said Alison. "It was great. We were treated to lunch at this fantastic restaurant, La Bonne Creperie in St Etienne de la Colline. Shame you couldn't make it. Jane was most upset she'd missed you."

I suppose it was galling to have needlessly spent so much of my available cash, especially when as a consequence I found myself humiliated into having to ask Matthew to make up the balance on my purchase of a Miko Parfait ice cream. But at least I'd not suffered the indignity of sitting on a coach all day next to Jane while she spent half her time flirting shamelessly with me and the other half whispering sweet nothings to Francois down her mobile phone. If that's true friendship then I'm the May Queen of Papworth Everard.

Tuesday 20th August

Spent the morning rehearsing for tomorrow night's concert. Father Beranger assured us that he has "worked ze oveurtime" to get a good crowd in. A well-earned siesta this afternoon, then a pleasant early evening tour of the town including the church and its crypt. The crypt contained an unusual feature, referred to somewhat quaintly by our tour guide as "ze nattering bookroom," but which Brian explained was actually the Whispering Library, so called because even the slightest whisper is said to generate an impressive echo. Sadly the library was locked so we were unable to test it for ourselves. The guide, despite his limited command of English, did made us all laugh when he told us the story of a boy who sang in the choir here a century ago, was known as Pierrot because he had such a pale face, and "who got ze sack for being caught unwrapping ze pie during ze sermon." Trust Henry Peasgood then to spoil the moment completely by asking him "Fruit pie, or Pie Jesu?" At least the guide was polite enough to pretend to find it funny.

The tour was followed by a meal with one of the other hosts, and then we all got together again for a drink in the bar where Jane was working. Barely had I sat myself down next to Julie than Jane came over to me and had the nerve to ask, in Julie's hearing, if I'd like to meet up with her on Thursday, our only other free full day this week. I was delighted to inform her that Raoul and Mariette have organised a day out for me already and I was therefore unavailable. Unfortunately no sooner had I shaken Jane off than Charles Tyrebuck appeared and insisted on asking me what I thought of the music of Gabriel Faure and the musical skills of the new assistant organist at Bradford Cathedral. In return, I was treated to a long and extremely tedious monologue on the parlous state of the foot pedals on the evidently antideluvian keyboard at Bolton Percy. It was no wonder that Julie muttered that she was tired and disappeared after five minutes.

I was congratulating myself on surviving my conversation with Charles Tyrebuck without either falling asleep or pouring a glass of wine all over him, when Lesley ambled unsteadily up to me, called for silence and said extremely loudly to me in a slow drawl, "What's Mr Footpump been telling you about Percy Bolton's instrument?"

This is turning into the longest week of my life.

Wednesday 21st August
Walked into town for our morning rehearsal, arriving a few minutes early. Julie was there as well, so I asked her if she'd like to meet up with me this afternoon. I had in mind a walk and something to eat. To my delight, she accepted. Better still, Jane was nearby and heard every word. About time she got a taste of her own medicine. We were very depleted for our rehearsal, but it was only at eleven fifteen, after singing for well over an hour, that Alison suggested some people believed we were rehearsing this afternoon rather than this morning.

"Great," snapped Tripplehorn. "We'll just have to rehearse this afternoon as well."

The upshot was that not only did I have to forgo my afternoon with Julie but by the time the concert was actually ready to start, I had sung the pieces over so often that the thought of having to perform them again made me feel quite ill. Evidently the Almighty thought the same way about having to listen to them, for as we prepared to reconvene for the concert, a large number of youngsters crowded into the church, carrying a variety of musical instruments and amplifiers suggestive of a major attack on the sensibilities, to say nothing of the eardrums, of the local populace. Father Beranger was quickly on the scene, but was clearly doomed to come out second best in the war of words between him and a bald-headed youth with a ring through his left nostril and clearly anarchic tattoos liberally splayed about his neck. Matthew thought it was hilarious and began commentating on it as though it were a boxing match. It didn't take long for the youth to strike the knock-out blow, for a moment later the priest came up to us and said that "owing to ze double-booking" we would have to hold our concert in the church hall instead.

Eventually we managed to scrape Tripplehorn off the ceiling and shepherd everybody via the crypt into the hall, but by then many of the would-be audience had evidently given up or believed, rightly or wrongly, that Byrd's *Ave Verum* and Poston's *Jesus Christ The Apple Tree* held less aesthetic pleasure than a French cover version of *Hit Me With Your Rhythm Stick*. Before an audience of no more than twenty-five, and minus Julie who'd somehow got lost in the confusion, we battled away manfully against what can only be described as a Babelesque cacophony that could be heard coming from the church, until our *a cappella* version of the hymn *Peace, Perfect Peace* came into head-on confrontation with *Come On Feel The Noise*. At that we decided enough was enough and we all, audience included, adjourned to the bar in the next room. Although Raoul and Mariette, who had come to see the concert, had settled down with a drink and seemed set to remain for some time, I was in no mood to stay any longer than we had to. And when I saw Jane standing behind the bar beckoning me to join her, I decided to go out in search of Julie and, if I didn't find her, walk back to the house for an early night using the key I'd been given. Unfortunately having made a dignified exit from the hall, using what I thought was a door that led out towards the street, I took a wrong turning and was soon hopelessly lost in the maze of corridors through which we had just passed. Before I knew it, I found myself back in church, now packed with aficionados of the St Pierre Sad Youth Retro Rock Society, who were sporting a variety of nostalgic garb from kaftans and hotpants to loud tartans and safety-pinned noses. It was perhaps a pity that the music had momentarily stopped, for no sooner had I entered than all eyes turned to me and everyone in the church erupted into laughter.

It was only then that I realised I was still wearing my choir robe. Thankfully the door on to the street was just a few feet away and amid cries of "Give us a song, monsieur!" and raucous attempts at the first line of "All zings bright and beautiful" I hastened to the main exit door, flung it open and hurtled off into the night. With any thought of attempting to pick my way back into the hall dispelled by the fear that I might become imprisoned among the chattering bookcases or terrify the elderly verger into thinking he had seen the ghost of Pierrot the Pie Cruncher.

Friday 23ʳᵈ August

After a lovely day out with Raoul and Mariette yesterday, together with Brian, Rachel and their hosts, it was back to earth today as we spent a hot, steamy, sultry morning rehearsing for our Sunday services. We are assured that last Sunday's TV drama has this week been replaced by mud-wrestling from Samoa, so we might even have a congregation for evensong.

Jane told me she was organising a barbecue at her lodgings later today and would I like to come. I had dreadful visions of a tanned Francois, stripped to his shorts and flipflops, massaging her with sun oil to the sounds of sizzling sausages while I hung about impotently in the background feasting off undercooked vegeburgers. I declined as politely as I could, and persuaded Julie to join me for what I hoped would be a thoroughly lazy afternoon, watching the world go by from one of the pavement cafes on the square. We duly ordered our meals and drinks, but, almost immediately after we'd done so, there was a tremendous clap of thunder and large drops of rain began beating down on our table. The awning offered precious little protection so we were all forced inside and found ourselves in a crush of bodies that could have passed for the Bakerloo Line in the Monday morning rush hour. I was all for fighting our way out and looking for something else, when suddenly I heard someone shout Julie's name and, turning round, I saw Samantha Ashton, accompanied by Dave and a lanky flaxen-haired young man who introduced himself to us as Jean-Paul. It turned out that Jean-Paul had been playing at Wednesday night's gig in the church and Julie had not only stayed to watch the gig but had got together with him, Samantha and Dave and they'd all gone out for a drink afterwards.

I noticed Julie eyeing up Jean-Paul lustfully almost from the moment she saw him, and it was no surprise when after an hour and a half of conversation in which I played virtually no part, she so readily accepted Jean-Paul's suggestion that we all drive to Bordeaux in his car for a meal and then a nightclub. Deciding that I didn't fancy playing gooseberry – or, as it looked to me, a double helping of gooseberry fool topped by luscious

122

gooseberry coulis and served on a bed of refreshing gooseberry jus – and rang Raoul, hoping for a lift home to avoid a soaking. There was no answer and I had no idea how or where to get a taxi so I decided to cut my losses and walk back through the storm which showed no signs of abating. When I got back, with rainwater dripping from every part of my clothing and what seemed horribly like the beginnings of a cold, they told me they'd not heard the phone, so glued were they to what was on TV. To be precise, Samoan mud-wrestling.

Saturday 24th August

Spent much of the morning in bed nursing a chill from my homeward paddle yesterday. Felt much better by lunchtime, and there was time for a bit of souvenir shopping prior to our rehearsal for the two services tomorrow. Father Beranger says that he can guarantee us a good crowd for evensong, so Tripplehorn hit on the idea of performing some of the pieces we had to omit on Wednesday as a sort of mini-recital while the punters were coming in for the service. "I know how disappointed you were to miss out on them the other night," he said, somewhat tongue-in-cheek. I don't think any of us would really have been that disappointed never to sing them again in our lifetimes.

Because we were travelling straight after evensong tomorrow, tonight was our farewell bash at the church hall, taking a similar format to last Saturday but with two host couples providing some traditional French chansons as the entertainment. By now resigned to having lost Julie as well as Jane, I was quite happy to share a table with Brian and Rachel. In fact neither Julie nor Jane present tonight, and Brian confirmed that Julie's staying on with Jean-Paul for another few days and not coming back with us. Alison mentioned that Jane had looked out for me in town this morning and had been sorry not to see me. That girl must take me for a complete moron.

I was nonetheless determined to put the setbacks of the week behind me and was enjoying a pleasant evening when, suddenly, Charles Tyrebuck materialised and sat down with me determined to get my opinions on the early works of Paul Hindemith and my perspective on the shenanigans involving the assistant curate and head chorister of St Something-or-Other somewhere just outside Market Weighton. Thankfully I was saved by the appearance of the entertainers, thus rendering further conversation impracticable. But with a long coach journey ahead of us tomorrow night and every opportunity for him to continue badgering me for my so-called expert views, I did feel constrained to mention as we were leaving that I wasn't really that knowledgeable about the history of French music or indeed the goings-on behind vestry doors in rural Yorkshire. He looked rather hurt and replied "Frank said you were something of an expert. As far as the French music's concerned, I was counting on you for help with this part of my Masters degree." "I don't know why he thinks I'm an expert," I replied. He frowned at me, drew in his breath and slowly asked "You *are* Henry Peasgood, aren't you?"

Sunday 25th August – *THIRTEENTH SUNDAY AFTER TRINITY*

Disaster. We foregathered in the vestry this morning to learn from Tripplehorn that owing to a 24-hour strike by French seamen all ferry crossings scheduled to depart from 4am tomorrow morning were cancelled. He had ascertained that there was space on the night crossing which departed well before then, and we all agreed that we must travel on that crossing, despite the fact that this would mean leaving almost immediately after church this morning and missing evensong.

As if that was not enough to take the edge off the enjoyment of our worship this morning, there was a grossly depleted congregation, owing to the fact that Father Beranger had persuaded most of his regulars to come this evening. The fact that a big cycle race, involving several riders of national repute, was passing through the town this morning didn't help matters either. Pre-occupied as we were by the latest turn of events, we made a hopeless mess of the mass and Samantha was two bars too early in her solo for the anthem, which meant that too was a failure. We were informed that we just had time to go back to our hosts, pack and say goodbye, and return to the square where the coach would pick us up at one o'clock sharp. It was an anticlimatical farewell to Raoul and Mariette, who have been wonderful hosts to me, but we promised we would keep in touch.

Jane was there to see us all off. I couldn't resist saying "I hope you and Francois will be very happy." She looked quizzically at me so I went on "Your fiance. Remember him?" "Oh, him," said Jane airily, "I packed him in ten days ago. I e-mailed you just before lunch on the Friday you came out and I've kept trying to tell you during this last week but you didn't seem interested."

The coach journey seemed much slower this time. We got stuck in two huge jams and I was getting really agitated about making it in time for the crossing. So tired and desperate was I to be back in England and to be enjoying the comfort of my own home that I even made one or two rash bargains with God regarding what I would do for him should he get me home in one piece next day. I sat miserably and apprehensively, trying to blot out the discordant janglings from the coach radio, Matthew's seemingly

124

endless quotes from *The Most Annoying Joke Book Ever*, and Lesley announcing to Rachel, in between fits of hysterics, the 99 different names she'd applied to Charles Tyrebuck during the week, comprising everything from Mr Tyrelever to Mr Puncture Repair Outfit in one of her less sober interludes. Had Margaret managed to magic a guitar from thin air and begun strumming *Amazing Grace*, and the line about "When we've been here ten thousand years," we'd have had the full set.

Sunday evening 25th August/Monday 26th August
We made it to the port with less than half an hour to spare, expecting absolute mayhem with hundreds of other passengers trying to do the same as us. On the contrary: the port seemed if anything on the quiet side, and there was plenty of space available for us. As we went up on deck, I expressed surprise to one of the crew and said in view of the strike I expected a far bigger crowd on board than this.

"The strike's next Monday," he replied.

So much for our choirmaster's command of the Gallic tongue.

Consoled myself with the thought that at least we were on our way home, even at the cost of missing out totally unnecessarily on both our final act of worship and any chance of patching things up with Jane. Perhaps more worrying are the things I agreed to God to do in return for getting home in one piece today. I suppose I can just about cope with singing a duet with Cora Willoughby-Smith at the Harvest supper following her earnest plea to me at the summer party. It's no great hardship to agree to sing for an ecumenical event the evangelical church is organising at the end of October, as requested by Margaret last Sunday afternoon. But I must say I blench at the very thought of having to own up to Hazel Ledworthy that I was the one responsible for breaking the point of her choir pencil before the service on the third Sunday after Easter.

125

SEPTEMBER

Sunday 1st September – *FOURTEENTH SUNDAY AFTER TRINITY*

A bizarre start to the month. We arrived at church to find Tripplehorn was away, and although Lesley said she knew he wouldn't be coming, nobody else seemed to be aware of the fact. Worse still, with Irving Cattermole absent, it became quite obvious that nobody had been nominated to play the organ instead.

Fortunately Joan Trumpington had with her the choir address book containing names of most, if not all, of the organists who had graced us with their presence in years past. Scrambling for our mobile phones, we took three or four names and numbers each and rang them. The results were not encouraging: five yielded either no responses or answerphone messages, the organists presumably playing at other churches, two had other engagements this morning, two had had to give up playing because of infirmity, and the other three were dead.

It was then that Joan had a bright idea. She mentioned that this had happened once before and they had got round the problem by using a cassette to provide the necessary accompaniment for the hymns. To her knowledge, the cassette and player were still in the vestry cupboard, and sure enough, a few moments' frenzied searching revealed a rather antiquated machine and a cassette entitled *Hymns Through The Church's Year*. Fortunately we discovered three hymns in succession that were not tied to a particular season, under the heading "Sundays After Trinity," and the fourth, *We Plough The Fields And Scatter*, was in fact wholly appropriate for this particular time of year.

A quick insertion of the cassette into the player at the right place, the location of a socket near the organ, and a speedy change of numbers on the hymn board, and the problem was solved. It was a shame that Joan inserted the cassette into the tape the wrong way – though foul play by Matthew could not be ruled out – so that instead of a playover for *Jerusalem The Golden* we got *God Rest You Merry Gentlemen*, and equally unfortunate that firstly the version of *He Who Would Valiant Be* bore no relation whatsoever to that in the hymn book, and secondly the cassette makers had contrived to find three extra verses of *The God Of Abraham Praise* which didn't appear in the hymn book at all.

As we were leaving afterwards I was accosted by one of the congregation, a middle-aged man who said to me "Most entertaining. Certainly more fun than the Organ Scholars' Masterclass I was giving in Winchester Cathedral last night."

Later I asked Joan why she hadn't put out an appeal to the congregation before the service. "Oh, I did," she said, "but I didn't hear anyone offer. Mind you, my hearing's still not right in my left ear so if someone to my left did volunteer I might have missed it."

I can't think why Tripplehorn hasn't given her the push years ago. Unless there was some part of "chocolate teapot" that her left ear also failed to register.

Friday 6ᵗʰ September

Our first full Friday choir practice for several weeks. Ken Foulkes was there tonight, having been persuaded to rejoin us for a few weeks because of a shortage of men's voices. Irving Cattermole is now on holiday for a month, and Gordon Hunnisett, who joined us towards the end of June, has written asking for a month's leave of absence in order to put the finishing touches on his book *Advanced Principles Of Formulaic Electromagnetism*. I can understand the rush to get the book out in good time for Christmas. I'm sure it'll be on the top of every book-lover's Yuletide wish list.

We had a look at my Harvest anthem tonight. Sadly, it had not won the radio competition but I was anxious for us to perform it all the same. To his credit, Tripplehorn had made a few minor modifications to it but had certainly stopped well short of rewriting it, and I was delighted with the murmurs of praise and appreciation which greeted his playover of the whole piece on the organ. Enthusiasm had wilted slightly after six unsuccessful attempts to get the first two pages right.

The organ did sound a little ropey during some sections of the playover and because, worse luck, there's a meeting of the PCC next Tuesday, Tripplehorn wants me to raise with them the question of funding for repairs to the instrument. "I shan't hold my breath," he said. "I see there are twenty-four items on the agenda already." He knows more than me. I've not even had my agenda yet.

A good pub session afterwards, enlivened by an exchange of photos and reminiscences from our week in France. Tripplehorn not in the least contrite about last Sunday, claiming he had arranged for Dr Jarvis of Stoney Marston – not in Joan's address book – to play in his place, and had told Joan this on at least three separate occasions. "Mind you, having said that, he always was a bit doo-lally," he said. "It wouldn't surprise me if he went to the wrong church by mistake – if he ever found the keys to his car."

It's nice that the musical side of our worship is in such capable, caring and compassionate hands.

Sunday 8th September – *FIFTEENTH SUNDAY AFTER TRINITY*
A slightly longer service than usual. Ralph Cameron and his wife Julia, stalwarts of the congregation throughout my time here, are off to Africa to help pioneer a project that will help village communities become self-sufficient in the production of food and water. They came forward to be specially commissioned and to ask for the prayers of our congregation, that their work in tilling and harvesting the land might be blessed. In the circumstances it would have been churlish to have denied their request for us to sing *We Plough The Fields And Scatter* for a second successive week. Received my PCC agenda this morning. Tripplehorn doesn't know what he's talking about. There weren't twenty-four items on the agenda. There were twenty-nine. With "choir matters" as item 28. In an effort to extend the hand of Christian brotherhood to Hazel Ledworthy, my predecessor on the PCC, I pointed to my item on the agenda and said with a laugh "That's obviously how importantly they regard us, then." "What do you mean?" she retorted testily. "Well," I said, now floundering somewhat, "did they always put choir matters so far down the agenda in your day?" "No," she said stiffly. "I made a list of specifics I wanted discussed in relation with the choir, and submitted them to the secretary three weeks beforehand. I usually found they were the first item after Matters Arising." I bet they were. The wretched secretary would not have dared put them anywhere else. Unless he had already made plans to live out the rest of his days as a yak-herd in Mongolia.

Tuesday 10th September
Dutifully dragged myself from my comfortable armchair to PCC tonight. I felt I really couldn't ask for priority yet again, tempting though it was to do so, and was only glad I had brought some work with me to do while the meeting was in progress. However, that only took me up to twenty to ten, and it was not in fact until ten to eleven that item 28 was called and all eyes looked expectantly in my direction. I had prepared myself thoroughly, writing down almost verbatim what I wanted to say in support of proper funding for essential repairs to the organ, and I had even incorporated a rather clever poem that Eileen Crosby, bless her, had composed concerning the debacle of nine days ago when there had been no organ for the service. I had written, I thought quite movingly, of the need for the musical side of our worship to be nurtured on the basis that it constituted a key aspect of our thank offering to God, and that with no organ we risked alienating the very people to whom we were trying to reach out.
I opened my mouth to begin my oration, when suddenly the chairman cut in and said "I think I can short circuit this. Frank Tripplehorn came to see me

this afternoon and he's agreed to obtain some estimates for remedial work to the organ. Clearly the work needs doing so we agreed that the Finance Committee will consider the estimates and decide to whom to award the contract. Everyone happy? Good. Right, item 29, Any Other Business."

I suppose the evening wasn't a complete write-off. I mean, how else would I have learned the night's red-hot sensational news, in advance of it being leaked to the international press agencies. That Mrs Dauntsey's hip operation may take her off the side-aisle carpet-vacuuming roster for the second quarter of next year.

Friday 13th September

Progress on my anthem still very fitful. Hazel Ledworthy whinging about how many high notes there are, totally out of her range. I wouldn't have thought it made any difference to her. If it's not something she knows, she never bothers to sing it anyway.

The new hymn books duly arrived this evening. If I hear one more reference to the appealing smell of the new pages, I may just have to torch the lot. Lesley was sniffing them voraciously like some crazed drug addict whose fix was long overdue, and even Rachel, who I thought a little more level-headed than Lesley, was drawing great nostrilfuls and lurching about waving her arms and murmuring "Peace, brother." I'm only grateful that Joan Trumpington appears to be happy to undertake the task of stamping PROPERTY OF ST BASIL'S PLEASE DO NOT REMOVE in each book, using her trusty stamp pad and ink that she once told me she has had fifty years. The smell of the stamping ink if it got outside the vestry cupboard would be enough to fill all the substance-misuse rehab clinics within a radius of fifty miles. Those that weren't already filled with the hymn book page sniffers, that is.

Sunday 15th September – *SIXTEENTH SUNDAY AFTER TRINITY*

Was somewhat mystified by the choice of hymns for this morning's service. Although I accept that the whole point of the new books is to provide us with a wider choice, *The Day Thou Gavest, Lord, Is Ended* seemed a strange selection for an act of morning worship, and *Glorious Things Of Thee Are Spoken*, to the tune *Deutschland Deutschland Uber Alles*, a little inappropriate for Battle Of Britain Sunday. And none of us were particularly chuffed at singing *We Plough The Fields And Scatter* for a third successive week.

It was only afterwards that we discovered that the vicar had forgotten we were now using the new books and had given Tripplehorn the hymn numbers as though we were still using the old ones.

I only hope the vicar doesn't make the same mistake for Saturday's wedding. And that we do not send the happy couple on their way either with the exhortation to *Fight The Good Fight With All Thy Might*, or warning of their *Day Of Wrath and Doom Impending*.

Friday 20th September

A busy practice tonight, with music to rehearse for Lord Buttermere's daughter's wedding tomorrow, and Harvest Thanksgiving on Sunday week. We have that morning off if we want it, but it's a three-line whip for the evening service at 6.30pm followed by a substantial buffet in the church hall and then some entertainment. Including a duet I've agreed to sing with Cora following the bargain I rashly made with the Almighty for getting us out of France last month.

We spent a long time on the wedding music. Chantal, the bride, decided earlier this week that she wants us to sing William Byrd's *Cibavit Eos* as an introit, on the basis that it was the first piece of music she heard with her fiance after they got engaged, in a church in Venice. I think we were all wishing, after struggling with it for over an hour, that the Venetian singers in the church of Chantal's memory had dispensed with their Renaissance polyphony in favour of a snappy unison burst of the Birdie Song.

Fortunately, the rest was straightforward, there being no particular problems with *Brother James' Air*, Stanford's Psalm 150 or Mozart's *Ave Verum*, while *Walking In The Air* is a straight solo. Apparently Samantha Ashton is to sing it, although I can't believe Cora, who was away tonight, gave it up without a fight. She's either had a sudden bout of laryngitis or Tripplehorn bought her off with a more than generous purchase from the duty free shop on the ferry back from France.

Nevertheless, it was twenty past nine when we finished and we'd not even begun work on my piece, despite the fact that Tripplehorn had twice during the evening told us that he wanted to spend some time on it. It was clear that everyone was getting restless and I have to say I was not surprised when he looked across to me and said "We're all very tired and it's too late to start anything else now. I really don't think we can do justice to your piece in the time we've got between now and next Sunday. May I suggest next year?" Without waiting to hear my reaction, Hazel Ledworthy growled "With pleasure" and tossed it aside like a piece of junk mail.

I'm sure Mozart never had this trouble.

Saturday 21ˢᵗ September

Predictably, the wedding of Chantal and Jeremy was a sumptuous occasion, the church magnificently decorated with beautiful flowers, all the men dressed in morning suits, and the ladies attired in a variety of colourful dresses and outrageous hats. I hadn't seen St Basil's so full since the midnight mass last Christmas.

Tripplehorn more agitated than usual. He said he had been on the point of ringing Lord Buttermere asking permission to ditch *Cibavit Eos*, only to be informed that one of the guests was a staunch member of the local Byrd Society. "So I think we're stuck with it," he told us beforehand. "Which doesn't mean to say I won't kick it into touch halfway through if it's all going pear-shaped." I don't think Byrd himself could have put it better.

Evidently, however, he felt that rather than disappoint the composer's avid fan among the guests, he might just as well let us plod on as long as we were singing something that approximated to what was on the page in front of us, and somehow we limped forlornly to the finishing line. We got off to a bad start with a duff soprano entry, and although we could be said to have got away with it by the skin of our teeth the overall effect was, it has to be said, fairly feeble. After that, we seemed rather to lose confidence, and even Samantha Ashton on her walk in the air seemed to be crying out for a parachute. Our performance seemed to cause even more colour to drain from the cheeks of the vicar, who apparently had been sick all morning and who looked none too healthy this afternoon. What should have been one of the most exciting events of the year was tinged with disappointment.

As we fought our way outside afterwards, Tripplehorn looked as angry as the thunderclouds that were busily gathering overhead. "Don't expect to be asked to sing at any more posh weddings," he snapped. "And as for what the Byrd Society think of us, I dread to imagine."

"I shouldn't worry," Lesley consoled him. "I've just found out it's not the local Byrd Society the guy belonged to. It was the local Bird *Sanctuary*."

Perhaps we should have done the Birdie Song then.

Sunday 22ⁿᵈ September – *SEVENTEENTH SUNDAY AFTER TRINITY*

No surprise to be told the vicar wasn't up to taking the service this morning, and that one of the posse of retired priests in our parish, Angus McGillicuddy, was stepping into the breach. By coincidence, he'd last presided exactly a year ago, and simply selected the same hymns again this year. The fact that he had been asked at short notice did not make the singing of *We Plough The Fields And Scatter* for the fourth successive Sunday any more palatable.

After the service Cora thrust an envelope into my hand and said "Our duet for the entertainment next Sunday, as promised. Frank's said we can sing through it on Friday after the practice."

My spirits were not raised in the slightest when I opened the envelope and found it contained a copy of *All I Ask Of You*, the famous love duet from *Phantom Of The Opera*. What a prospect. Standing up on the church hall stage on a blowy Sunday evening, with *Coronation Street* on telly and work next morning, my stomach full of Queenie Haverthwaite's pumpkin and gruyere quiche, competing for both volume and stage space with the self-styled Diva of St Basil and as convincing a lover for her as a tub of ripe Happy Shopper cottage cheese.

I only hope I can find some way out of it by the weekend.

Friday 27th September
Grabbed the bull by the horns first thing this morning and telephoned Cora. Told her that all week I had been troubled by the fact that *Phantom Of The Opera* is still very much in copyright and that we could find ourselves in difficulties firstly by photocopying the music and secondly by performing it without a licence.

"I think you'll find there's no difficulty," she replied. "I cleared it weeks ago with an old friend of mine who knows a little bit about the law." I immediately thought of Cyril Potts, a doddery retired solicitor who murders the first lesson every couple of months. "It wouldn't be one of our readers, would it?" I asked, permitting myself a caustic chuckle. "The Attorney General, actually," she replied. I suppose it was worth a try.

After reconciling myself during this week to having the performance of my Harvest anthem postponed for twelve months, found my feelings of resentment bubbling up again tonight when I discovered what Tripplehorn had decided we should sing instead. Scrawled on loose manuscript paper, it was a quite preposterously cheesy ode to the well-filled garners of freshly gathered wheat, the orchards fair blooming with rosy apples, the golden corn waving seductively in the sun-kissed valleys, and the sweet rain falling benevolently upon the sheep-filled pastures. After we'd sung through it for the third time I said jovially "Are sick bags provided free with this music?" Tripplehorn frowned at me and replied "I think it's a shame that the cynical world of the new millennium is so quick to ridicule the divinely inspired outpourings of a composer endeavouring to put into words his boundless praise for the bounteous gifts that God has bestowed upon his earthly children."

132

Stung by his rebuke, I shut up. Later in the pub afterwards, I told Lesley how dreadful I felt that I had so decried the work of one so obviously consumed with joy at the majesty of God's abundant grace all around him.

"I wouldn't worry," she said. "Frank wrote it himself the other day. Sitting in a traffic jam on the M11."

Sunday 29ᵗʰ September – *EIGHTEENTH SUNDAY AFTER TRINITY – HARVEST*

It seemed strange not singing with the choir on a Sunday morning for the first time this year. Out of habit, went along to the morning service, a predictably rather flat affair. Cora insisted on putting on her robes and singing in her usual place, effectively creating a choir of one. She even sang Greene's *Thou Visitest The Earth,* which is one of my favourite anthems. Or was until today.

The evening service was, however, a huge success. Mrs Bundy and her team had worked tirelessly all afternoon getting the church ready, and when we arrived at five thirty for our final practice, the church was filled to bursting with produce, flowers and greenery. This is always a well-attended service and tonight the church was packed solid, so I was especially disappointed that my anthem had bitten the dust. One could tell who the casual visitors were. They were the ones who actually needed their hymn books for the words of *We Plough The Fields And Scatter.*

A magnificent spread awaited us afterwards. No pumpkin and gruyere quiche, but Queenie Haverthwaite's stilton and beetroot concoction worked surprisingly well, particularly when washed down with some excellent French wine. As I was replenishing my glass, intending to have just a drop more before moving on to fruit juice, Lesley hurried up to me with a message from Jane which had been e-mailed a couple of hours ago. It seems she is desperately homesick at university, is thinking of packing the whole thing in, and needs me to go up and see her as soon as possible. She hinted I should be prepared to take her home afterwards. Further, she said that she understood completely why I had been so off with her during our week in August, and in fact she rather liked my mean and moody attitude. She signed off with numerous kisses.

So elated was I that I permitted myself another full glass of wine, which with the two I'd had previously caused me to approach the love duet with considerably more passion than was necessary or indeed appropriate. The net result of clasping Cora tightly to my bosom was not only that I got the full force of Queenie's Garlic Mushroom Surprise which I'd seen her tucking into ten minutes previously, but also an earful of piercing high notes the noise of which reminded me of the sounds I unwittingly generated from Maria Callas when at the age of four and a half, while my grandad was playing me one of his 78s of Grand Opera at La Scala, I trod on the turntable.

Perhaps another night stranded at the ferry port would have been more agreeable after all.

Monday 30th September

Managed to make phone contact with Jane this morning, and have agreed to meet her in the car park outside her hall of residence at eleven on Saturday. I remembered from my previous visit to the city that there is a quite excellent music shop, Carruthers Music Supplies, close to the campus, and I may well be tempted to splash out on some sheet music for my own collection. Decided it would be courteous of me to ask Tripplehorn if there was anything he would like from the shop while I was there, but I quickly wished I hadn't, as he e-mailed me back half an hour later with a list of about thirty items. A lot of it was fairly well-known stuff, which I'm surprised we don't have in our library, but I'm not too confident how successful I'll be in tracing some of the more obscure pieces such as *Appropinquet Deprecatio* by Albrecht Feuchtwanger, or *That I Might Pick Ripe Cherries* by Cyril Chetwynd Dibble. Especially if I'm served by a teenage Saturday shop assistant who thinks a libretto is the latest Italian forward to sign for Arsenal.

OCTOBER

Friday 4th October
With Harvest now behind us, the next two big events are the choir outing on October 19th, two weeks tomorrow, and the recording which will be spread over the first three days of November. The recording's being done by Queenie's grandson, Ben, who's training to be a professional sound recordist, and tonight we looked at some of the pieces we're going to offer to posterity. It's all very stock material, the theme being the Church's Year with pieces for Christmas, Passiontide, Easter and so forth. It seemed rather strange, doing *While Shepherds Watched Their Flocks By Night* when the Harvest decorations were still up in the church. "No sock-washing, please, Matthew," Tripplehorn said sternly. Tactically it was a grave error, for this merely seemed to encourage him to greater heights of groan-inducing word-play. After four run-throughs the shepherds had made no inroads into their hosiery cleansing but had blotched their frocks, botched their mocks, notched their pocks and, presumably recalling memories of the Battle Of Culloden, scotched the Jocks. Fortunately we got on to something else so were spared any speculation by Matthew as to whether it was possible to "crotch" anything or anyone. Moreover *Gabriel's Message* is not on the list, which is just as well. Two house-to-house carol-singing evenings' worth of most highly flavoured gravy is enough for any grown man.

Saturday 5th October
At least the roads were nice and quiet at half-past four in the morning.
Arrived at the university at ten thirty after a slow crawl up the last three miles of motorway in a most unseasonal heat. I did at least four laps of the main drive through the campus – there really was no call for the Murray Walker impersonation I heard from a waggish student as I raced past the Student Union bar for the fourth time – before finally locating the car park where Jane and I had agreed to meet, and was then forced to pay the exorbitant flat daily rate for a stay I hoped would be no more than ten minutes. True to her word, Jane appeared at the appointed time, accompanied by a hirsute youth sporting a long scruffy leather coat and with rings dangling from each ear. "I tried to phone you first thing but you'd gone," she explained. "This is Bilbo. We met at Freshers Disco last night. I love this place now. Thanks for coming anyway." Having uttered which, she slipped her hand into Bilbo's, and together they wandered off towards the bar.

Consoled myself with the thought of a good browse in Carruthers. Found the premises quite easily, only to find that it had since my last visit been converted into a fast food restaurant by the name of the Mr Porker Burger Palace.

Made some enquiries and discovered that Carruthers had gone out of business four months ago, but a new music shop, Musarama, had opened three streets away. I located it speedily enough, but one glance at the window display of electric guitars and drums and the paucity of shelf space given over to sheet music of any description suggested a very different type of establishment from the now sadly defunct Carruthers.

I decided to confine my requests to the more straightforward ones on Tripplehorn's list, so I approached the solitary assistant, a tall gormless-looking blonde, and asked her if she could supply me with Stanford's *Beati Quorum Via*.

"Pharmacy's next door," she replied.

Sunday 6th October – *NINETEENTH SUNDAY AFTER TRINITY*

A much happier day today. A glorious, very warm, sunny morning, a full choir, a good congregation, an excellent sermon, topical and heartfelt intercessions, a nice psalm with a lovely chant, one of my favourite mass settings, a good anthem and no hymns that provided the opportunity for Cora Willoughby-Smith to screech the last three notes up the octave.

No *We Plough The Fields And Scatter*, thank goodness. I half expected the *Guinness Book Of Records* to have taken an interest. It wouldn't have been the first time, either. Arthur Ramsbottom was telling me that in 1989 the choir tried to set a world record for the longest consecutive period of hymn singing, only to find that nobody had actually been present to verify the record attempt, the scrutineer having taken a wrong turning off the North Circular and Joan Trumpington allowing the record attempt to start anyway, not realising that the official-looking man sitting near the front of the church with clipboard and pen was merely there to read the gas meter.

Friday 11th October

A shorter practice tonight, virtually all of it spent on music for our recording. We then adjourned to Brian and Rachel's for a bring-your-own plate supper and a choir video evening. I noted with some trepidation the appearance of Arthur Ramsbottom and an inordinately large quantity of cassettes of choir outings, but hoped that the video of the French trip would occupy so much of the evening that we wouldn't actually get to his collection at all.

The film show started well, as Rachel produced a tape her brother-in-law had done of the choir to send to his cousins in South Africa. It had been shot in May, quite unbeknown to us, and I have to say we came over quite impressively. Tripplehorn then dug into the archives and produced a camcording of a wedding the choir had sung over eleven years ago, again to a very high standard. We then settled back in anticipation of an enjoyable re-living of our recent adventures in the Dordogne.

Things certainly started well enough, with some breathtaking camera shots of some of the finest scenery in the area, and Handel's *Water Music* by way of accompaniment. We then cut to the church in which we'd sung, and were treated to several minutes of Craig Dumbleton, whose hosts had made the film, sitting alone in the choirstalls in turn scratching his head, licking his lips and chewing at a pencil. Following that, there was an interminable scene that appeared to have been taken in the host family's residence, incorporating Craig assisting in the preparation of frog's leg soup, and then attempting to read aloud from a French newspaper dressed only in his flipflops and a pair of orange underpants. That piece of footage alone should have prompted someone to warn viewers in advance that the film wass unsuitable for persons of a nervous or sensitive disposition, and display a contact number on the screen afterwards for the benefit of those who had been in some way affected by what they had seen. However, when asked if there was any more film involving other members of the choir, perhaps actually doing some proper singing, Craig was only able to respond "Not to my knowledge."

I think even Arthur Ramsbottom himself was taken aback by the warmth of the welcome he received when inserting into the machine his 1985 tape of The One Where A Passing Crab Nearly Found Its Way Into Avril Codrington's Salmon Paste Sandwiches.

Sunday 13th October – *TWENTIETH SUNDAY AFTER TRINITY*

Alison Sparkes' niece Alicia was baptised during the morning service. It was wholly appropriate, therefore, that Matthew should sing the solo in Margaret Rizza's *Grail Prayer*, while Zoe added some flute accompaniment to make it a real family affair. I never realised what a lovely pure treble voice Matthew had. He sang the solo quite beautifully, and as a choir we complemented it very impressively, creating an effect that was inspiring and moving. Just as satisfying was seeing the flustered look on Cora's face after the service. She must feel her monopoly on the solo for verse 1 of *Once In Royal* at the Christmas carol service, which I am told she has had for at least the past twelve years, is about to be broken. The punters are predicting the closest battle in years: the established favourite challenged by an upstart from the younger generation. It wouldn't surprise me if Ladbroke's took an interest. Over coffee afterwards it was clear that Cora was already feeling the pressure, being overheard saying to Hazel Ledworthy "Of course, we all know what happened twenty years ago when young Justin Merridew attempted that solo verse. With so much at stake, an even mature temperament and a steady nerve must prevail."

I told Alison what I'd overheard and asked her if Justin had indeed let the side down at the crucial moment.

"Er – yes," she replied. "Although he did remarkably well considering he'd been told seconds before opening his mouth to sing that Oliver Ormondroyd had inserted a tubful of itching powder down the back of his neck."

I can't see many prisoners being taken on this one.

Friday 18th October

Gordon Hunnisett has resigned from the choir. From his letter, which was passed round during the practice, you'd have thought he was our most valued member rather than someone who'd attended just three and a half rehearsals and no more than four Sunday services. He wrote of the "deep wrestling between myself and my conscience as I contemplated the magnitude of my decision....difficult questions of prioritisation on my spiritual agenda.....deep agonies pervading my soul in reconciling my earthly responsibilities and godly duties." He's clearly wasting his talents writing about electromagnetism. He ought to be signed up by Mills and Boon.

The good news is that Ken Foulkes has agreed to stay on pending the appointment of a new bass to sing with Irving, Henry and Brian. In the pub afterwards, I told Ken it had always troubled me that he'd not had a proper farewell sendoff following his decision to resign earlier in the year, and there were murmurs of agreement from around the table. "Cedric Skeffington had a tremendous farewell do before going up to Scotland to live," mused Lesley. "His own choice of hymns and anthem, a special presentation at the end of the service, cakes with the coffee, and even a mention in the intercessions." "Presumably," I said, "To thank God for enriching the congregation of St Basil's with his devotion and loyalty?" "Yes," said Rachel, "and to thank God he was going."

Saturday 19th October

The day of the choir outing had arrived at last. Our destination was the lovely Dorset town of Lyme Regis, with its famous sea wall known as the Cob, last visited by me a good twenty years ago.

Apparently a number of traditions have grown up with the choir outing. The first, before we left in the morning, was the Coachbuster Sweepstake, with each of us placing bets on firstly whether anyone would be left behind by the coach at some point in the day – it has apparently happened four times in as many decades – and secondly, if it did happen, who the "coachbusted" traveller, as it was called, would be. If nobody wins, the stake money is donated to charity. Although there was some divergence of opinion on who might be coachbusted this time, I was moderately re-assured that nobody seemed to be betting on it happening to me.

A rather longer journey than I'd hoped. Henry Peasgood had requested a detour to visit the church at Ryme Intrinseca, which, I heard him announce at least five times, is one of only two in the whole country that is dedicated to St Hippolytus and it was for this reason that he was particularly anxious to see it. It was a pity that the church was locked and an extensive search failed to trace either of the keyholders. Henry unfortunately chose to take it rather badly, and insisted on venting his frustration on every occupant of the coach, including Joan Trumpington who was navigating, so it was with great relief that we finally arrived at the seafront. I was slightly surprised to see neither the Cob nor any of the other distinguishing features of Lyme, and it was only after a rather perplexing ten minutes that someone thought to accost a passer-by and ask if the Cob had been washed away. "As far as I know it's still there," he replied, "but it's Lyme Regis you'll find it, not here in Charmouth."

I'd heard of Joan taking drivers down the wrong street but never into the wrong town. Perhaps we should have been grateful she'd not transported us into the wrong universe. Next year maybe.

At last we got there and enjoyed a well-earned drink, following which we embarked on another choir outing tradition, namely the Conducted Tour, which this year consisted of a visit to a fossil exhibition and shop. Not everyone was enthusiastic – Lesley was heard to comment that we look out across a sea of old fossils every Sunday morning – and I must say the tour did go on a very long time. As we finally left the shop for the traditional Choir Picnic Lunch I set a good fast pace, only to be stopped in my tracks by Arthur Ramsbottom, camcorder in hand. He had evidently escaped the fossil tour, perhaps afraid of being hauled in as an exhibit, and insisted on taking me aside to film me providing an appraisal of the day so far. Realising that any refusal to co-operate or indiscreet comment would be immortalised in future video showings possibly generations from now, I duly obliged, glossing over the more hideous aspects of the proceedings. Arthur was clearly loving every second, ending his interview by saying "Well, much may happen down here in the next four hours, but, for now, thank you," as though he were filming the SAS preparing to storm an aircraft that had been forced by armed terrorists to land in the gardens of Buckingham Palace rather than the St Basil's choir outing. Then off he went in determined mood, clearly desperate not to miss Cora spilling her coffee in the Cosy Nook Tea Parlour or Irving Cattermole arguing with the Happy Newsagent over the price of a packet of pipe tobacco.

By now the rest of the party had disappeared. Still, this gave me the perfect pretext to escape further regimented activity, of which I felt I'd had more than enough, and enjoy some time off on my own, beginning with a civilised lunch and then a good walk along the undercliff path to the west of the town. Realised that having missed the picnic I didn't know the exact time of our rendezvous for the return trip, but based on Arthur's "four hours" comment I saw no problem in getting back to the coach park well ahead of the hour of our departure, and indeed I had what I considered to be ample time to spare as I returned to town following my walk. As I passed the Royal Standard pub, I happened to see Brian and Rachel through the window, so decided to join them and we ended up enjoying a couple of pints. I was about to offer to buy a third round when Brian looked at his watch and said "Shouldn't you be on the coach now? By my watch it should have left five minutes ago." For a moment I thought it was a wind-up. "Well, if I've missed it, so have you," I said. "We're not catching it," said Brian. "We're staying on for another couple of days and my sister's meeting us and taking us home."

Despite my frantic dash to the coach park I was too late.

I suppose I should have been grateful that a few moments later the coach miraculously re-appeared, Rachel having had the good sense to call Lesley's mobile number and alert the driver. But as we made our way homeward, I realised that in fact the cost of a taxi to the nearest railway station and a train ticket home, a long wait for a train, and an even longer wait for a connecting service, getting me home possibly three hours after everyone else, would have been a small price to pay for avoiding firstly the ridicule I received for being the first one to be coachbusted since Audrey Manningham-Ogilvy in 1982, and secondly the traditional On-The-Way-Home-Sing-Song. I have never known Sullivan's *The Long Day Closes*, Passareau's *Il Est Bel Et Bon*, Pitoni's *Cantate Domino*, or Polly Perkins of Paddington Green, to have been bludgeoned quite so mercilessly. And even brave men would have recoiled at the devastation that resulted from the bloody assault on the *Holy City*.

Sunday 20th October – *TWENTY FIRST SUNDAY AFTER TRINITY*

Not surprisingly, we were somewhat depleted this morning. Arthur Ramsbottom, who has seen and done it all on choir outings and is obviously able to take them in his stride, was there, and Craig Dumbleton made it too, but not a single alto turned up. I thus volunteered to sing alto, and Tripplehorn, who seemed delighted that the geriatric contingent in the choir was so greatly reduced today, readily agreed. It was quite fun singing falsetto again, for the first time since entertaining the Wolverhampton Polytechnic glee club's Bring-and-Sing Summer Barbecue, even though the alto parts this morning were almost all on one note.

Over coffee I was chatting to a couple who had come down from Lancashire. They seemed very subdued, and indeed were in the area for the saddest of reasons: the husband had just lost his mother very suddenly and the funeral was taking place in a nearby village tomorrow. She was apparently a contralto member of that village church choir for many years.

As we were talking, Tripplehorn bounded up to me and thanked me for my assistance this morning. I commented that the music had hardly been what one might call challenging. "Ah, you know what they say about altos," said Tripplehorn. "They're the ones who in heaven are polishing up the harps while the sopranos are learning all the decent tunes."

I suppose it could have been worse and he could have come out with his variation, "There are no altos in heaven as God gets bored listening to the same two notes all day." The husband tactfully said nothing. As for me, I don't think I can ever have taken such a keen interest in the fluff content of the right sleeve of my jumper.

Friday 25th October

A busy but enjoyable evening's rehearsal for next weekend's recording. I love practices where we cover lots of different music without dwelling too much on anything in particular. Some of the music hadn't been sung for years and appeared, on the strength of what I'd been given, to date back to the reign of a choirmaster who insisted on the rigorous use of pencils to mark instructions in copies. One of my pieces of music tonight had so many instructions, half of which appeared to contradict each other anyway, that it was hard actually to discern the notes; one had copious drawings including, above the syllables "minibus" of the Latin word "hominibus," a dormobile trundling along a country lane; one contained an assortment of intriguing messages, from "Not Cod Or Lard"(presumably referring to the optimum mode of pronunciation of "God" and "Lord") to "Don't Look At Oliver Ormondroyd" above the single syllable "Tart" of "Tartarus" at the end of a page; and one contained so many depictions of pairs of spectacles, by way of reminders to watch for tricky corners or entries, that it looked less like a page of music than a drawing of an optician's shop window.

Felt in such good spirits at the end that I was pleased to confirm my agreement, with some other choir members, to form part of a group Margaret has convened to sing some plainchant and a couple of extracts from Faure's *Requiem* at an ecumenical service in the town's Roman Catholic church to mark All Souls Day next Wednesday. We meet this Sunday evening to go through the music. Traditionally we have kept All Souls in St Basil's by a special act of evening worship, but this year Tripplehorn has persuaded the vicar to transfer its commemoration to the nearest Sunday, with the names of the departed loved ones of the choir and congregation being read during the normal morning service. He told us he was concerned at the traditionally poor evening attendance and felt that as many as possible should be in church to honour those who were no longer among us but who during their time on earth had enriched the lives of those around them.

"Of course, we all know the real reason," he said over a gin and tonic in the Holly Tree half an hour later. "The list of people who've snuffed it is getting so long that if we started in the evening we'd be there all night."

Sunday 27th October – *TWENTY SECOND SUNDAY AFTER TRINITY*

The extra hour in bed this morning was certainly most welcome. Craig Dumbleton missed out on it, having forgotten to put his clock back an hour, and judging by the large number in the congregation as I arrived twenty minutes before the service, he wasn't the only one.

As part of our preparations for the recording, we sang what must have been a record six motets this morning, including an introit, offertory motet, and six communion motets. They included John IV's *Crux Fidelis*, which was intended to be sung at Passiontide, and *Hodie Christus* by Sweelinck which is a Christmas piece. The congregation didn't bat an eyelid. "I suppose if it's in Latin you can get away with it," I said to Lesley afterwards. "With this lot, you could have sung in plainchant the first eighteen items of the menu in the Rising Star Tandoori and got away with it," she replied.

Rehearsal in the Catholic church tonight for the service on Wednesday. I'm sure I recognised the guy sitting next to me from that dreadful service I'd sung at in January in the evangelical church during the week of prayer for

Christian unity. His voice was no more pleasing to blend with than Arthur Ramsbottom's, and his under-arm area a good deal more pungent. The choir leader was a pleasant but rather diffident middle-aged man who reminded me a little of Sergeant Wilson of *Dad's Army* as he asked the sopranos if they "would mind awfully if we could just go back to that rather lovely entry two bars after letter B." We got through the Faure quite easily but spent a very long time on the Latin plainchant. The choir leader asked for a little more expressiveness in the chanting, prompting one of the other choir members to say "It would help if you could tell us what the words mean in English." It was too good an opportunity to miss and I responded "Crispy duck in tangy orange liqueur sauce." I'm glad to say Ken laughed but as for the rest, I'd have got more laughs out of an Albanian debt collectors' convention.

Wednesday 30th October
We were asked to be at the RC church at six for a one hour rehearsal which included a practice for the rather elaborate procession. One would have thought this was a royal funeral, judging by the amount of time the priest insisted on taking with it. Having dutifully marched up and down the church a good six times, and rehearsed the Faure and the plainchant what seemed like twice that, we sat and awaited the crowds.....all fourteen of them.
We sang well enough for the early part of the service but the choreography was another matter. Although we had rehearsed the plainchant and the procession copiously, we had not actually practised them together. I had also failed to appreciate that during the procession to the memorial, the church was being darkened and we were carrying lighted candles. To make matters worse, because of a mix-up further down the line, I found myself leading the procession. Quite unable to see where I was going and follow the music at the same time, it was no wonder that I wandered magnificently off course, tripped over a loose stone, and crashed to the ground.
Tried to make light of it afterwards with the walking deodorant advertisement by saying "I suppose there is that psalm which goes 'O come let us worship and fall down.'" He looked at me as though I were an overcooked turnip dumpling and walked away.
Over a much-needed drink afterwards I asked Margaret if she knew him. "Oh yes," she said, "He leads his church's Wacky Kiddies Holiday Fun Club."
I hate to think who leads their funerals.

NOVEMBER

Friday 1ˢᵗ November – *ALL SAINTS DAY*
Walked down the church path this evening with Margaret, apologising for at least the third time for my nosedive on Wednesday night, and expressing relief tht the malign influence of Hallowe'en had not extended to my street or indeed the town to any great extent, if the local news this morning was anything to go by.

"I think I must take credit for that," she said. "We had a special Alternative Hallowe'en Party at the evangelical church youth club last night. We threw the invite open to anybody under 18 who wished to come along. Free admission, lots of entertainment, great food and a really good talk on the dangers of black magic and witchcraft. I really think what we said rubbed off on most if not all of them. It was a huge success."

Which was more than could be said for the start to our first recording session. We arrived, as agreed, at 6.50 for 7 only to find a said mass for All Saints Day still in progress. There were at least twenty-five in the congregation which seemed very high for a said weekday celebration. With a choir we could surely have doubled it and made it a really good act of worship. I commented to Brian how this contrasted with Ash Wednesday when we laid on a choral mass and less than half a dozen had turned up. "Presumably they weren't told there was a choir that night?" I asked him. "Probably not," he replied, "but you know how these things leak out."

It wasn't till nearly quarter to eight that we finally got going, and even then we inevitably had a slow start as Ben, our recordist, needed to check levels and decide where best to situate the mikes. Sensibly, Tripplehorn had chosen five or six easy pieces to start us off and give us confidence, with just one tough one, Palestrina's *Sicut Cervus*, at the end, but even just this one piece really did test our endurance levels to the limit. We attempted at least six recordings but each time we came unstuck somewhere in the middle and had to retake. At long last we made what looked certain to be a perfect recording, and it was with great satisfaction, bordering on almost celestial delight, that we found ourselves proceeding smoothly on to the last line of the music. Only for three boys to burst into the church, their faces covered with hideous masks, shrilling "Trick or treat!" at the tops of their voices before laughing manically and disappearing back out into the night. There being no suitable gap in the piece from which re-recording was possible, it was back to the top for an eighth time. Or possibly ninth.

Better luck next year, Margaret.

Saturday 2ⁿᵈ November

As I was leaving the house this morning, I got a phone call from Jane, saying she was down from university for a few days and would I like to meet her for a bite to eat this evening. Mindful of the debacle four weeks ago, and the fact that I might easily be playing gooseberry with her and Bilbo, I was tempted to refuse. But my social life outside the existing choir membership is virtually zero at present, so I agreed to collect her from her house at seven thirty.

Ben, our recordist, had his tutor, a short middle-aged man with a ruddy complexion and thick black moustache, overseeing his operation this morning. The result was calamitous. The young man who yesterday had been a self-assured very professional operator suddenly turned into a gibbering wreck without any of his previous confidence. His tutor did not help in the slightest, castigating him for the tiniest mistake and treating him with the mixture of irritation and contempt that a Roman emperor might have reserved for a mosquito fluttering around his breakfast table. It was no surprise when Ben announced, totally unnerved, that after two and a half hours' recording of some of the most difficult pieces in our repertoire, he had inadvertently wiped the entire tape.

Through tremendous hard work and concentration, and helped by the fact that the tutor had gone and Ben was now back to his old self, we found ourselves only an hour behind schedule by lunchtime, and agreed to take a slightly shorter lunch to reduce the deficit by a further fifteen minutes. A further blow awaited us, however, in the form of Sylvia Faraday, a musical friend of Tripplehorn's who had agreed to supplement our numbers for the afternoon pieces, for all of which there were two soprano parts. On the face of it she was extremely friendly and enthusiastic but the tone for the afternoon was set when, after we had done a perfectly acceptable recording of our first piece, she said "I don't think we quite got that *diminuendo* on bar 16 and surely there needs to be a dynamic contrast between the *rallentando* at bar 29 and the *adagio* section three bars after letter C. Shall we try it again?" Whether it was *ritenutos, sforzandos, glissandos,* arpeggios or Caravaggios, her command of musical terms, declaimed with a somewhat affected Italian accent, seemed to know no bounds and it was all I could do, when she mentioned the need for a strong tessitura, to ask if it was best served with tonic water or tomato juice.

The upshot was that we finished the recording not at six thirty as agreed but seven forty five. Two or three people had already had to leave, but after the way Jane had messed me around four weeks ago, I had no compunction about staying on to the end of the session even though it would mean keeping her waiting. When I phoned both her home and her mobile there was no answer so, assuming she had decided to go out with Bilbo instead, I had a meal at home and then joined some of the choir members in the Holly Tree.

When I arrived, Jane was just leaving, her arm wrapped round a young man whom I vaguely recognised as another former youth group helper. She explained that when I didn't turn up, she'd rung him and he was taking her for a drink and then dinner and a club. "Think you've missed out there," said Lesley as she walked past me on her way to the bar.

I asked Jane what had happened to Bilbo. "Oh, him?" she said with a laugh. "I dumped him a week after you last saw us. No, actually, it was the next day. See you at Christmas perhaps."

Sunday 3rd November – *FOURTH SUNDAY BEFORE ADVENT – ALL SOULS*

Singing Victoria's *O Quam Gloriosum* in the service this morning seemed quite a relaxing exercise after the pressure of the recording. It was good to know that the crash of a pencil or book to the ground would not have to result in a retake, as it had done at least three times yesterday.

Sylvia Faraday back with us again today, singing in the service and recording with us this afternoon. Quite a kerfuffle this morning when she did not go up to receive communion. Whilst it is common for some members of the congregation, particularly those who have turned up simply to hear their banns read, not to go up, I've never known a choir member to decide not to do so. Hazel Ledworthy muttered afterwards, not realising that Sylvia was immediately behind her, that whatever one's religious belief, as a choir member one had a duty to be seen to be going up to the communion rail, if only to receive a blessing, thereby demonstrating the choir's corporate nature and its commitment as a single body to leading the worship. Sylvia rounded on her and said "Some of us received communion at the eight o'clock service." There was a tense silence, during which I contemplated either running for cover or calling for an armed response unit, but Hazel seemed to know that she was beaten and merely walked angrily away. Over coffee I asked Sylvia if she had in fact been to the eight o'clock service. "Of course not," she said, "but it shut the old trout up."

We could use her in the choir every Sunday.

It had been a long service, with the addition of the list of names of the departed, so Tripplehorn suggested we started recording at twelve thirty, not twelve as originally planned. It of course meant we finished half an hour late. Sylvia much more subdued this afternoon – I think Tripplehorn,

147

mindful of the need to finish in good time for the *Antiques Roadshow*, had asked her to curb her enthusiasm – but towards the end we were all getting tired and irritable and it was clear that the quality was beginning to suffer. We duly finished the schedule of planned items and were beginning to pack up, when Tripplehorn announced that he wanted to record just one further item. Unbelievably, he produced Herbert Bumfrey's setting of *Ave Verum* which we'd not looked at in rehearsal at all but had cursorily hurried through during the April workshop. If we read through it once, we read through it fifty times. If we tried recording it once, we tried recording it a hundred times. By the time we'd finished, the *Antiques Roadshow* customers had long since hurried home to re-insure their camel-shaped carriage clocks, Edwardian picnic baskets and Victorian wind-up dogs.

As we were leaving I said to Tripplehorn "I hope all the people who buy the tape appreciate the toil that went into that one." "Oh, we won't use that on the recording," he said airily. "I just thought it'd be fun to do, that's all." Absolutely. For entertainment value, right up there with gold-prospecting in the central reservation of the M42.

Tuesday 5th November

PCC tonight. Choir matters had leapfrogged to number 14 on the agenda, well up the hit parade, but stuck uncomfortably behind two longstanding favourites – Contribution To Diocesan Quota (item 9) and Condition Of Graves In Vicinity Of Basil's Oak (item 11) – and a brand new entry at item 13, Impact Of Decision In Lanyard v Braithwaite On Disposal Of Surplus Incense Ash.

With a long day at work tomorrow, including an evening meeting, felt justified in asking to be released after Choir Matters had been dealt with. I was quite looking forward to speaking positively about the success of the recording sessions and the boost that sales of the CD will give to church funds in the run-up to Christmas. But I never got the chance as, when my item was introduced at the commendably civilised time of nine twenty, Florence Juggins straightaway demanded of me "Why has the choir booked the church between 4pm and 7pm on 22nd December for rehearsing for the carol service the next night when it's well known that that is the evening of the town's Christingle Service in the church?" I told her I knew nothing about it. "I can't accept that," she said. "You must know where the church bookings diary is kept." I said in that case the whole thing was a misunderstanding, whoever booked the church for the practice must clearly have overlooked the Christingle service, and I was sure that we could rehearse at some other time. "Oh, it's too late now," said Florence. "We've

148

had to move the Christingle Service forward a fortnight. People won't be in the Christmas mood. I just think it's such a shame." To my great discomfiture, others nodded sagely and said that it was "yet another" example of the choir imposing its will unilaterally on other church members. After having been harangued for what must have been a good fifteen minutes, I was forced into giving assurances that attitudes among choir members and organisers would indeed have to change radically to ensure firstly that nothing like this would happen again and that the concept of the choir as "leading" the worship did not extend to their taking over the administration of wider church affairs and threatening the very fabric of the church community.

Decided it would not be a good move to even mention the CD. On the strength of tonight, I can't see Santa dropping it down many PCC members' chimneys.

Even though it was ten twenty when I finally got back, I rang Tripplehorn and told him about what I'd just been through. "Oh, that was Joan, bless her heart," he said. "I asked her to book the church for the *early* afternoon of the 22nd . She was going to phone you this evening and tell you it's all been sorted and the Christingle service has been reinstated on the 22nd. She must have forgotten. Never mind."

I informed him that thanks to her the reputation and status of the choir amongst the church hierarchy was now somewhat lower than the colony of dung beetles that have taken up residence just to the south-east of the vestry door (item 8).

"Oh, they'll get over it," he said. "As long as you gave a good plug for the CD, that's all that matters to me."

He might not feel the same way when I advise the PCC exactly where they can dump their surplus incense ash.

Friday 8th November

A shorter practice tonight because of our firework party, and the available time was spent on the music for Remembrance Sunday. Cora cautioned the children about the need for absolute quiet during the two minutes' silence – I think she only feels the need to do it because one wretched child let out a rather violent sneeze during the silence back in 1972 – and also mentioned that this year the mayor will attend the traditional parade at the War Memorial by the south door on horseback. Henry Peasgood was moved to comment "We'd better all pray that during the silence there's no snuffling, no snorting, no rumblings from the rear, and no little accidents on the pavement." Zoe replied, a little too loudly, "That's enough about Joan Trumpington. What about the horse?" We then adjourned to Rachel's for the party. We enjoyed letting off a goodly supply of rockets and Catherine wheels, tucked into sausages on sticks and toffee apples, and contributed generously to Christian Aid as a thanksgiving for a fun evening. Nobody seemed in a great hurry to leave, and Rachel, our hostess, was on the point of making drinks when I noticed a ghastly gleam in Arthur Ramsbottom's eye. Suddenly, like the villain in a suspense movie whipping a gun from his pocket, he produced, seemingly from nowhere, a videotape with the dreaded words CHOIR OUTING TO LYME REGIS inscribed on the label, and inserted it into the VCR. To have made an excuse would have seemed too farcically transparent, as only a moment or two ago I had accepted the offer of a brandy, so I was forced to stand and wait, like a condemned prisoner at the steps of the guillotine, bereft of all thought save a numbing dread for the unavoidable ghastliness of the ordeal to come. Suddenly, as the first shaky picture of the coach hit the screen, accompanied by an excruciatingly tinny "We're All Going On A Summer Holiday" as the wonderfully apposite soundtrack, there was a loud bang just outside the window, and a succession of agonised screams. Immediately Rachel shouted "Stop the tape! There's been an accident!" and the more able-bodied ones among us hurried outside, to discover a shocked and frightened Matthew. It became apparent, in the course of the tearful conversation that followed, that he'd been on the way back to the car with a doggy bag from the party when a stray firework had gone off without warning. Mercifully, he hadn't been hurt, but it had certainly shaken him, and so anxious in turn were the rest of us that we immediately decided to call it a night.

As Arthur Ramsbottom disappeared down the drive in his rusty Renault Five, I said to Matthew "Well, at least you got us out of watching that video." He gave a mischievous grin, withdrew the remains of a burst balloon from his pocket and said "I know. Good, wasn't I?"

Not perhaps one for the CV of an aspiring carol service soloist. But I think I owe him all the same.

Sunday 10th November – *REMEMBRANCE SUNDAY*

A muggy, drizzly morning, totally in keeping with the sombre nature of this morning's worship. I have always felt uncomfortable singing patriotic hymns on Remembrance Sunday with the implication that all those who lost their lives did so for a common noble cause, whereas history has shown how hopelessly futile so many of the sacrifices proved to be. I was relieved that this morning's music focussed more on the need for peace in the world and the help of God in times of distress. As we sang Croft's *Funeral Sentences* followed by Purcell's *Thou Knowest Lord*, I thought of the men much younger than myself, less than a century ago, being forced away from their jobs, their homes, their families and their loved ones simply for the privilege of battling with each other to gain a few extra hundred yards of mud, at the behest of incompetent generals miles behind the front lines. The image was so powerful that for a few seconds I found myself barely able to sing. And curiously I quite resented being coaxed out of my reverie by Queenie Haverthwaite's spectacular coughing fit on the final page of the Purcell. At least it made me feel a little better about my mobile phone going off in the middle of the two minutes' silence.

Friday 15th November

Tonight we began work on the Christmas carol service. For the past four years it has taken place the day before Christmas Eve, in the early evening, and each time it has been packed solid, the large numbers enticed not only by the beauty of the music and the festive atmosphere but the mulled wine and mince pies served in the church hall afterwards. Apparently up until four years ago the carol service had always taken place on Boxing Day, on account of the local clergy's view that the celebration of Christmas should begin at the midnight service on Christmas Eve, and not before. However, as Lesley explained, there were significant theological reasons for abandoning this somewhat rigid stance. "Of course," said Margaret. "The bodily revelation of the Lord to humanity is a constant never-changing reality and each day a Christian awakes he celebrates the appearance of Christ to him in his glory and his humility." "Yes, that as well," said Lesley. "More important, the carol service kept clashing with the *Fools and Horses* Christmas special."

Saturday 16th November

Going through my music this morning, noticed that my copy of *Carols For Choirs* volume 1 was in a particularly dog-eared state, so decided to drive to the music shop where I'd bought the hymn book at the end of January and purchase a new copy. The shop had lots in stock, but there was a long wait to be served, behind a group of students buying instrumental pieces for exams. I passed the time studying a poster on the wall advertising a very attractive CAROLS OLD AND NEW concert with seasonal refreshments, to be given sometime next month by a group calling themselves Cantemus, billed on the poster as "the most exciting *a cappella* group in the South." As I was looking at it I was accosted by a tall distinguished-looking man who told me he recognised me from my fine alto singing in St Basil's four weeks ago. He explained to me that his name was Peter Copplestone, and he was in a bit of a spot: he'd been let down just an hour or so ago and was desperate for an alto soloist for a performance of Handel's *Messiah* taking place tonight in Fordhurst Hall in a village some eighteen miles away. I could hardly believe it when I heard him say that Cantemus was organising it. Of course I accepted at once and having shelled out £12 for the carol book, went straight home to start preparing myself.

Slightly nonplussed to arrive at Fordhurst Hall, for which I had been given excellent directions, to see that it was not a country house but a community centre, and even more surprised to enter the main room to find it in total darkness. I did, however, hear some noise round the back, so made my way behind the stage to discover another, smaller room, full of elderly people sitting at tables with plates of food on each. Assuming I'd come to the wrong place I was just about to leave when I saw Peter Copplestone offering a nonogenarian a plastic plateful of hula hoops. Made a beeline for him and asked where the concert was taking place.

"Oh, in here," he said. "It's very informal. We put the tape machine on and everyone sings along to the chorus bits. When it gets to solos, you just sing along with the soloist on the tape. We couldn't get a soprano soloist in the end so everyone can join in those." He looked apologetically out across the assembled company. "We're running awfully late I'm afraid. Eileen Butterworth forgot to put the sausages in so the buffet got held up. We'll get going after the notices and the raffle." I asked him where Cantemus came into it all. "Not Cantemus," he laughed. "Gandremus. Our local Gramophone And Recorded Music Society. The Singalong *Messiah* is one of the highlights of the year."

It was difficult to identify the lowest point of the evening after that. It could have been the 40-minute wait for the notices and raffle and the offer to me in the interim of the full run of the buffet, from lukewarm underdone chipolatas to curling coronation chicken sandwiches. It might have been the 15 minutes it took to read the notices, covering such weighty topics as the card going round for Gladwys Pringle with her haemorrhoids and the overdue instalment payments on the Christmas outing to see the premiere of the locally-written play *Slop Goes The Weasel* by Mavis Gussage. Or the 20 minutes it took to complete the raffle, with no person in the room capable of ascertaining whether they had the winning ticket without the number being read out at least four times. Or the moment I was asked, as guest soloist, to present a raffle prize and found myself holding aloft a pair of bedsocks for which no self-respecting market-stall holder would have dared to charge more than 20p. Or the exclamation by one old dear when I commenced the aria *But Who May Abide* "Oh, this one goes on far too long, can't we fast forward it." Or the uninvited assistance I received as I sang *O Thou That Tellest*, some of the assembled company clearly believing it to be either a soprano solo or a chorus. Or the treatment that two geriatrics at the table nearest me meted out to the florid soprano aria *Rejoice Greatly*. Or the moment when after I'd declaimed the opening words of the aria *He Was Despised*, which I had practised at length during the afternoon, Peter Copplestone switched off the tape and announced that we would have to cut straight to the Amen Chorus because we had to be out of the hall in ten minutes on the instructions of the caretaker Mrs Boggis. Or the presentation to me of my reward for the evening, namely a bottle of evil-looking cheap plonk with a yellow post-it-note marked ALLTO SOLIST stuck on the side. Personally I think the gold star went to the geriatric couple I was told by Peter Copplestone wanted to see me specially, and who demonstrated their recognition of my musical contribution to the enjoyment and success of the evening by asking if I'd yet had time to mend the cistern in the downstairs ladies' toilet.

Suffice it to say I have no plans to be anywhere near Fordhurst Hall on the 29th March when they do Singalong-a-*South Pacific*.

Sunday 17ᵗʰ November – *SECOND SUNDAY BEFORE ADVENT*

A wet morning, a below-average congregation, and a poor stab at Stravinsky's *Ave Maria*. Worse, I found that I'd missed Jane who'd come down for the weekend but had gone back up this morning. The good news is that next Sunday there's to be a double baptism, which should up the numbers considerably on the first day our CD and tape are on general sale at church.

Ken Foulkes sidled up to me afterwards. "Shame you couldn't make it last night," he said. "I tried phoning you at half six but you'd gone out. A music publisher friend of mine was down and I'm sure would have been very interested in your Harvest anthem. I dragged Lesley, Jane and Frank round and we had a light supper and musical evening. Jane particularly sorry to miss you." Inwardly fuming, I asked him if his publisher friend was still with him. "Sadly no," Ken replied. "He flew off this morning for three months. In Moscow. Pity."

I explained that I'd love to have joined them, but something else had come up. "It's a bit of a long story," I said, "but it all started with going to buy a *Carols For Choirs* book."

"Oh, I see," said Ken. "Funny you should mention it. I saw a pristine copy of volume 1 in the Help The Aged shop yesterday morning. For fifty pence."

Monday 18th November

Tripplehorn phoned during the morning, in a state of great excitement, to tell me that he's organised a special launch party for the choir's CD and tape on Thursday evening.

"Whereabouts?" I asked him, my mind's eye surveying the vast crowds milling impatiently but excitedly outside HMV Oxford Street and the ranks of glitterati, surrounded by photographers and journalists, being ushered into the store from all corners of the entertainment world.

"Ray's News N Records, Bagley Road," he replied.

Well, I suppose even Robbie Williams had to start somewhere.

He went on to explain that Thursday evening sees the first of five consecutive Thursday Christmas shopping nights in town in the run-up to the festivities. He wants all the choir members to attend not only to talk to the punters as they come streaming through the doors, but to offer drinks and nibbles the money for which he has somehow wangled out of the PCC. He is also delegating to some of us the task of publicising the event through the media, and asked me if I would contact the local radio station.

If I tried ringing the station once, using the phone number in the local directory, I must have tried thirty times, but with no response. Eventually, convinced I was dialling the wrong number, I tuned into the radio station itself and seconds later heard the announcer say, "Call us NOW on......" – a completely different number. Rang it and almost immediately found myself talking to a girl announcing her name to be Nikki and asking "what do you think the answer is?"

It sounded a rather deep philosophical question for an overcast Monday morning in November, and I struggled for a moment to think how best to formulate a response that acknowledged man's unending search for meaning and purpose and quest for absolute truth amidst the bewildering mysteries of the unfolding universe. Playing for time, I asked if she could clarify the question.

"Of course," she said. "What number was the Army Surplus Special in *Wacky Races*?"

From the subsequent conversation it soon became obvious that I'd rung through to that morning's phone-in switchboard, and what made it worse was having to display my total ignorance of the correct answer. Nikki, however, couldn't have been nicer and promised she'd connect me direct with the right number. I held on patiently for ten minutes, only to be

154

informed by Nikki that she was having problems with the internal phone system and that she thought it probably best to give me the number of the special direct line. Which turned out to be precisely the one I'd been dialling for the last half-hour.

Cora phoned me later asking me if I'd contacted Darren Pack from the *Doorstep Journal*, the weekly free newspaper, about Thursday. I had the greatest of pleasure telling her nobody had asked me to contact him and if my experiences in trying to interest the local radio station were anything to go by, I would probably have more success in marketing it to the snake-eating pygmies of the Upper Congo.

Thursday 21st November

We duly foregathered at Ray's News N Records to be met by the manager who was in a refreshingly upbeat frame of mind. He told us the only competition we had in town tonight appeared to be from Reg Bullivant who was doing a signing session for his magnum opus *Could You Repeat The Question Please? – A History Of The Crown & Anchor Wennington Road Pub Quiz Team* at the bookshop two doors down.

The manager's mood was decidedly gloomier two hours later. In those two hours we had managed only seven sales, five of these to church members who'd have bought them on Sunday anyway, one to the manager as a present for his niece in Australia who had a hearing defect, and one to a lady who later brought it back to us for a refund having mistakenly believed that we were the choir of St Basil's Cathedral, Moscow.

As we set off down the road, having decided to call proceedings to a halt thirty minutes ahead of schedule, I noticed a large queue stretching from inside the bookshop out into the street. At the head of the queue, inside the shop, was a table piled high with copies of *Could You Repeat The Question Please* and an overweight middle-aged man busily signing them for the horde of eager patrons.

Felt somehow compelled to join the queue and pay for my own copy. When I finally came face to face with R. Bullivant Esq. I asked him how he had succeeded where we had manifestly failed.

"Simple," he said. "A nice write-up in today's paper. They were a bit short of copy so I got a good spread."

"Which paper?" I inquired.

"The *Doorstep Journal*," he replied.

Friday 22ⁿᵈ November

Copies of the CD were on sale to the choir this evening: one free one each plus however many we wanted at a special reduced price. It was certainly good to get two thirds of my Christmas shopping done in the space of three minutes.

We had a really enjoyable practice tonight, as Tripplehorn got us to sing lots of carols from which he will decide which ones we do at Christmas. We didn't spend more than five minutes on any of them and probably got through a good couple of dozen. Many were old favourites but towards the end we sang through several that were completely new to me, including one quite ghastly piece, *In Fleshly Form*, full of discordant clashes. Tripplehorn summed it up nicely when he said "If it sounds right, you're probably singing it wrong." I turned to Irving Cattermole and said "He's really scraping the barrel with this one, isn't he? Who on earth wrote this rubbish?" "I did," he replied.

We finished with two more popular carols, Michael Head's *Little Road To Bethlehem*, where someone had endorsed my copy with a drawing of a motorway and signpost saying BETHLEHEM 2200 MILES SCRATCHWOOD SERVICES 1 MILE, and Herbert Howells' *Here Is The Little Door*, where a simple rectangle had been drawn in the middle of the front cover. I asked Craig if he knew what its significance was. "It's obvious," Henry Peasgood butted in. "If that is the little door, that's the letter box in the middle. I rather think I drew it myself."

He really ought to get out more often.

Sunday 24ᵗʰ November – *SUNDAY NEXT BEFORE ADVENT*

A fine crisp sunny day. With a large turnout for the baptism service and the Christmas lights now on in town, it was not surprising that the mood among the congregation was buoyant and generous, and we sold out of CD's this morning. We made a complete pig's breakfast of the anthem and the vicar was able, during the notices, to make a joke of it, saying "You heard the choir mess up the anthem this morning – why not hear them get it right on CD!" I suppose it doesn't matter that the anthem wasn't actually on the CD at all.

Matthew and Cora auditioned for *Once In Royal* this morning. When I heard Matthew's beautiful treble voice, with the purity of driven snow and the texture of soft silk, I had visions of heavenly angels descending serenely from on high and offering a foretaste of celestial bliss. When I heard Cora all I could think of was the sound I heard the time I saw a steamroller flatten a brace of pigeons in Thames Ditton High Street.

156

A few minutes later, as we were drinking our coffee in the hall, Tripplehorn rushed excitedly in and revealed to us that he had persuaded Cora that she was not up to the required standard and that Matthew would be doing the solo verse. I looked hard for signs either of deep flesh wounds or a bullet proof vest but he seemed strangely unscathed. We were just offering our congratulations to Matthew and pouring him a celebratory orange squash when Cora walked in, helped herself to a coffee and marched over to Hazel Ledworthy. "Of course, the audition was nothing to do with it," I heard her say. "I'd advised Frank just beforehand that I've another engagement on the evening of the carols. Compering and singing at the Bushmead Hill Residents' Association Tuesday Afternoon Over Sixties Ladies Club Christmas Party. Far more important." And with that she flounced off.

I don't know who I feel more sorry for, Tripplehorn or her. Or indeed the members of the Bushmead Hill Residents' Association Tuesday Afternoon Over Sixties Ladies Club.

Friday 29th November

To supper with Ken Foulkes and his wife before tonight's practice. Over coffee, after a delicious meal, he asked if I'd like to team up with Margaret, Lesley, Rachel, Brian and himself for carol-singing one evening before Christmas. "I thought the whole choir went carol-singing," I said. "Well, yes," replied Ken with a smile. "If what you mean by carol-singing is knocking on the same twelve doors each year murdering the same six carols each year. I'm planning something a bit more ambitious. We meet here to rehearse on the Sunday afternoon before, then on the night we drive out to the next village which as you know has some lovely houses and an excellent pub. We tour the village and end up at the pub for a final sing and a cherry brandy on the house to see us on our way." I told him it sounded a fantastic idea. "I hope so," he replied. "No Joan Trumpington to muck up the arrangements. No Arthur Ramsbottom and his wretched camcorder. No Cora Willoughby-Smith demanding to do a solo descant on every last verse. And no Henry Peasgood saying how he made five thousand pounds from singing carols at three houses on one night in 1975."
I can't wait.

Surprisingly low on men at tonight's rehearsal, with Henry Peasgood, Craig Dumbleton and Brian Ellis all missing. During the practice we were reminded of all our Christmas choir diary dates: carol-singing on 17th December, our choir Christmas party in the hall after the practice on the 20th, and the carol service itself on the 23rd, following a rehearsal on the afternoon before. We have our big midnight eucharist on Christmas Eve, followed by a family service on Christmas Day itself. There's no choir as such on Christmas Day; this is so that choir members can either enjoy the service with their families, or sleep off the exertions of the night before, though apparently the formidable triumvirate of Cora, Hazel and Joan usually sing in the choir anyway. Although there's enough in the coffee money kitty for some party fare for the 20th, I've also been asked if at Tuesday's PCC meeting I can put in for some cash for the party from church funds. It's quite a big do with ex-choir members traditionally invited as well as families. Another, rather nice, tradition is for each choir member to put a favourite carol on to a piece of paper and Tripplehorn will promise to incorporate each one either into the big carol service or the midnight eucharist. That is, subject to it still being available in printed form, being within the choir's capability, and having some Christian content. For some reason, it is all done anonymously. Nominations closed at the start of tonight's practice, having been invited since last Friday, and Tripplehorn announced the results this evening. The usual suspects – *Silent Night, In The Bleak Midwinter* ("Harold Darke please, not Holst"), *Away In A Manger* and *The Holly And The Ivy* were all there, plus *Good King Wenceslas*, my own choice, and some less well-known ones including what sounded like an Italian carol, *Confezione Monodose Da Non Vendersi Singolarmente*. Composer unknown.

"The initials H.P. have been put after it," said Tripplehorn. "Plus a note that he's lost the only copy he ever had. Trust Henry Peasgood to bowl us a googly. Has anyone else heard of it or would they know if we had it?" There was a deafening silence. "Well, I've not been beaten before," he went on. "Joan, if you'll look out our archives, and I'll ring round one or two of my experts in London tomorrow. Hopefully Henry will have some idea where he last performed it."

Throughout the rest of the practice he seemed in a rather subdued mood, as if annoyed that a piece of Christmas music had been identified that he was unfamiliar with.

In the pub afterwards Rachel sidled up to me and said "I hope he's not looked too far. Apparently it was Matthew's doing."

"How on earth does Matthew know so much about Italian music?" I queried.

"He doesn't," said Rachel. "He copied the words off a packet of an individual-sized portion of strawberry jam."

DECEMBER

Sunday 1st December – *ADVENT SUNDAY*

I always like Advent Sunday, with the promise of Christmas just a few weeks away. The Advent traditions are well observed at St Basil's – a simple procession to the plainchant Advent antiphons, emphasizing the timeless message of the coming of God to mankind in human form; the lighting of the first candle on the Advent wreath, symbolising the triumph of light and hope over darkness and despair; the presentation of Advent calendars to the children, these simple gifts making their faces light up with innocent youthful joy; and slogging through all seven verses of *O Come O Come Emmanuel* before having to repeat the first verse at the end for good measure.

Despite the continued shortage in the lower parts, Ken also presenting his apologies this morning, we sang passably well before an excellent congregation. Quite a thought-provoking sermon from a guest preacher, who invited us to think not only of Jesus' coming to us as a baby, and as our Judge at the end of time, but also how what we might say to him if he came as an ordinary human being and stood among us in church.

"That's easy," I heard Tripplehorn murmur. "I'd give him a folder and get him to join the basses."

Tuesday 3rd December

Woke with a sinking heart at the realisation that it's PCC tonight. After a pretty foul day at work, I decided I couldn't face it and rang the secretary to present my apologies, intending then to phone the treasurer to ask if the request for extra money for the choir party could be discussed in my absence. Since I'd not even received an agenda for the meeting, I didn't exactly get the impression that they were desperate for me to be there anyway.

"It'd be a pity if you couldn't come," the secretary told me. "We're having our PCC Christmas party this evening. It's one of the highlights of the year. Still, if you're not feeling up to it...."

I assured him that, with the prospect of sherry and mince pies, good music and good company, I was now feeling really much better.

Was not sure exactly what to expect when I got round to the hall, but assumed that there would be a reasonable party atmosphere. So I was somewhat dismayed to find just a handful of the membership grouped solemnly around a table upon which was nothing more than a couple of bottles of supermarket wine, a carton of convenience store orange juice, and

159

a paper plate with a morose heap of peanuts and an equally uninspiring assembly of potato crisps. If that's what they call one of the highlights of the year, I hate to imagine what they're like when they've got something to be miserable about.

Decided to make the best of a bad job and was chatting quite amiably to Eleanor Percival about the dry rot in the head brass cleaner's cubby hole when the secretary crept up behind me and said "So sorry to interrupt but we ought to start our meeting now." I'd assumed the party WAS the meeting, but now found myself the proud owner of an agenda with 31 items on it, choir matters being number 28. "I would have put you nearer the top," the secretary said, "but when you told me on the phone how much better you were, I felt I could leave things as they stood."

Having had no chance to broach the subject of the extra choir party cash with the treasurer thus far, I had no choice but to sit it out.

Even with eleven items adjourned to the next meeting because the chairman of the Churchyard Maintenance Committee was away, and a further four put off because we were awaiting the outcome of a consultation report from the Diocesan Quota Management Sub Group, it was still gone ten forty, and I was on the point of losing the will to live, when we reached item 28. I duly made my request and, to my amazement and delight, the treasurer agreed to it at once without it even going to a vote.

I had done it. I had achieved something at a PCC meeting.

As I made my way home, I decided that this must rank as one of my lifetime achievements, up there with my school athletics cup for winning the 400 metres, and that first kiss from Debbie Wainwright. And possibly even on a par with my 2000-word article in *Buses And Busmen* about my 15-hour, 230-mile tour of Staffordshire on a £1.95 Busadayaway ticket.

Wednesday 4th December
Wasted no time in ringing Tripplehorn with the news.

"Oh, I know," he said airily. "I was at the Finance Committee meeting on Monday night when they agreed it."

Resisting the temptation to ask why on earth he hadn't told me before last night thereby saving me a completely wasted evening, I asked him how he'd managed to persuade the notoriously stingy Finance Committee.

"Like I always do when they're not with me on something," he replied. "We sit discussing the pros and cons, weighing up all the arguments, then after reflecting maturely, soberly and evenhandedly on the evidence in front of us, we all agree that I was right in the first place."

Thursday 5th December

It's not often I tune into my local radio station but this morning I did, just catching the *Thought For The Day*. The speaker, a local lay preacher by the name of Garth Postlethwaite, challenged us to think of someone who has upset or troubled us lately, and extend the hand of forgiveness and brotherhood towards them. I decided to take up the challenge by contacting Hazel Ledworthy tonight and sharing with her my concerns about my usefulness on the PCC. I reckoned that under her brusque, harsh exterior was a lonely, insecure woman and decided she might perhaps welcome the opportunity to feel wanted for advice, and even to be asked once again to accept the responsibilities of choir representative.

Although I had prepared myself thoroughly, even going as far as writing down everything I was going to say, it was still with considerable trepidation that at just gone half past seven I dialled her number and, following a terse "Yes" by way of answer, told her who I was.

"Who?" she barked.

I repeated my name and launched into my prepared speech. "I feel as if I really haven't contributed much at all to the work of the PCC," I told her. "I feel isolated and unwelcome. Choir items always seem to get left to the end and when they are discussed it often seems they've been dealt with in advance of the meeting or someone raises something I can't deal with. I just wonder if either you could give me some advice based on your experience as to whether there's anything more I could or should be doing to improve things, or whether you feel you'd like to take over from me after Christmas when the PCC next meet and use your experience and familiarity with the other PCC members to improve the profile and standing of the choir at the meetings."

My heart was pounding, my palms were glistening and my knees were knocking as I waited for her response.

"Who are you again?" she demanded.

With all the steadiness and cool composure of a jellyfish being eyed up by a giant squid, I told her my name for a third time and repeated my pronouncement.

"I can't talk to you now," she snapped. "I'm waiting on the plumber for my faulty stopcock."

Perhaps I'll stick to Terry Wogan in the mornings in future.

Friday 6th December

Despite Tripplehorn being in a bad mood because half our set of *Carols For Choirs* II has gone AWOL, we had a good sing tonight. The carol service is already taking shape extremely well. Ken sang *Three Kings From Persian Lands Afar* quite beautifully. I was delighted to be singing the *Carols For Choirs* versions of *The First Nowell* and *See Amid The Winter's Snow* which I've always found drag excruciatingly when every verse is sung exactly the same.

No sign of Queenie Haverthwaite for the third successive Friday. Tripplehorn was moved to comment on it as we neared the end of the practice. "She is getting on a little, poor soul," said Eileen Crosby. "Perhaps she thinks enough is enough at her time of life." "I doubt it," said Tripplehorn with feeling. "Knowing her as I do, I suspect the only way she'll be leaving the choir is in a wooden box."

At that moment the vicar entered, stood diffidently in front of us, and said "If I may interrupt, I fear I have some sad news. I thought as choir members you ought to be among the first to know. I'm sorry to tell you that Queenie Haverthwaite died an hour ago."

To see the look on Tripplehorn's face would have been worth travelling from far beyond Persian lands. Amid any amount of the wrong type of winter's snow.

Sunday 8th December – *SECOND SUNDAY IN ADVENT*

It was a very subdued choir that lined up for the service this morning. I noticed shock on the faces of quite a few of the congregation who were informed of the news of Queenie's death through the weekly pew sheet. Although Queenie wasn't the greatest singer, she was a very sweet-natured old lady with many friends in St Basil's. And on a more prosaic note, it's fair to say that without her we would never have managed to get the recording done so efficiently and economically. The funeral takes place on Friday afternoon and although I've a couple of meetings planned at work, will cancel them to make sure I can be there.

Originally we'd planned to sing the exuberant Hassler motet *Dixit Maria* this morning, but after earnest discussion beforehand decided to cancel it and sing Howard Goodall's setting of *The Lord Is My Shepherd*, one of Queenie's favourites, instead.

The vicar, it has to be said, was marvellous, saying a prayer for her soul as the second Advent candle was lit. I felt a lump in my throat as we contemplated the marvellous message of hope and anticipation that Advent-tide brings, while at the same time committing Queenie to the Lord in the hope of life immortal in his glorious presence. I happened to looked across at Cora Willoughby-Smith at that moment and saw that she was in floods of tears. Afterwards I commented to Rachel that I didn't realise that she and

Queenie were that close. "To be honest with you," she said, "Cora only started speaking to her again last Christmas. After two and a half years." "I had no idea Queenie could upset anyone quite so much," I remarked. "Well," she replied, "you try waiting till Cora's just about to start a solo rendition of *Sheep May Safely Graze* during the town's civic service in the presence of the town Mayor, Lady Mayoress, the county's Lord Lieutenant, the principal of the Royal College of Music and two High Court judges, and then unwrap a brand new packet of Strepsils."

Tuesday 10th December

Was hard at work this morning when I received a phone call from Lesley with an SOS. Her sister works at a care home just outside of town and on the second Tuesday afternoon of each month they have guest entertainers. This afternoon they were expecting a visit from Leonard Antoniello, real name Mick Samways, to sing a selection of seasonal favourites, but over the weekend he had tripped over a high note in *Cavalleria Rusticana*, had lost his voice and was quite unable to sing. Could a deputation from St Basil's possibly come and sing a selection of carols from the *Carols For Choirs* book for half an hour or so, with tea and mince pies to follow.

The debacle at Fordhurst three and a half weeks ago was still fresh in my mind, but on the basis that it was for just half an hour I agreed, even though it meant re-arranging yet another meeting.

Quite a good number of us had managed to get there: Eileen, Cora, Rachel, Margaret, Lesley, Craig and Henry were all present, with an assembled audience of roughly twenty. Undeterred by some snores from the back row and a very audible "Is there any escape from this?" from one green-jacketed octogenarian depressingly near the front, we kicked off with a passable *O Come All Ye Faithful* and *Once In Royal*. Somewhat rashly, Lesley then invited requests. At least two ladies promptly piped up that they would like to hear *We Three Kings Of Orient Are*, only for us to discover that the carol wasn't in our books at all and we thus had to improvise. Fortunately at least one of us knew the words of every verse, and it was with this spirit of co-operation in mind that we busked our way not only through this carol but some others that were perhaps understandably conspicuous by their absence from the carol books we had brought with us, including *Rudolph The Red-Nosed Reindeer*, *Knees Up Mother Brown* and *Mademoiselle From Armentieres, Parlez-Vous*.

Somewhat wearily, Lesley asked if there was a more traditional carol they would like, and in response *Silent Night* was suggested by a foreign-sounding lady near the back. Accordingly, we happily reached for our carol books – only to find that that wasn't there either. "Never mind," said the lady, "I will sing it to you." She then proceeded to give the most beautiful rendition of the first two verses in German, her voice strong yet mellifluous. "Before I sing the last verse," she said, "Let me tell you a story about this carol. My father was sent to the Russian front in the last war. He was called to the front just before Christmas 1941. On Christmas Eve we were in our home together as a family, and he asked me to sing to him. I had learnt this carol, *Silent Night*, by heart at school, and with the snow gently falling outside, and the little fire burning in the grate, I sat by the fire with my mother and my father around me and sang it. He then got up, kissed me tenderly on the cheek, and a moment later he had gone out of our lives."

I noticed that the room had gone very quiet and every eye was fixed on this small but keen-eyed old lady, all of us evidently anticipating the climax of her story with a sense of fear and unease.

"We heard nothing from him for years," she said. "Then after the war, he came back. He had been captured and taken prisoner. Somehow he survived. I had every certainty that he would. I drew my inspiration from that memory of the three of us sitting by the fireplace in our little home, singing to him those wonderful words about a little child who came to save us from the sins and evils of man."

With that, she proceeded to sing the last verse. As the final note died away on her lips, there was an intensely moving silence, a silence of reflection on the brutality of war, which saw her family torn apart, contrasted with her spirit of courage and hope that the Christmas message gave to all mankind for all time.....

A silence broken by Mrs Green Jacket demanding "Aren't we missing *Countdown?*"

Thursday 12th December

A day off today. I had planned to give much of it over to finishing my Christmas cards and doing Christmas shopping, avoiding the Saturday crush. We were also having our choir practice a day early this week out of respect for Queenie, whose funeral was tomorrow. I found as I got going on my cards that I only had choir members left to do and was getting rather low on my De Luxe Charity Selection pack, with its fine illustration Plainsong Adoration depicting angelic figures darting between lines of medieval chant. For the privilege of receiving one of these particularly appropriate cards, I selected Brian and Rachel Ellis, Lesley Markwick, Ken Foulkes and Margaret Pardew, all of whom have been so kind to me throughout the year. That left just one more in the pack, and I could not decide whether Frank

Tripplehorn or Craig Dumbleton should be the lucky recipient. Sadly for Craig, I had been unable to find a selection pack containing a depiction of Santa and his reindeer hovering merrily over a snow-covered Effingham Junction station car park.

As I was pondering this, Tripplehorn phoned me and asked how busy I was today. Before I could answer he told me there was a carol he had unearthed, *Greet The Gladsome Morn*, that he was desperate to get put on to computer by tonight's practice. He said "I have an aversion, as you know, to trying to read carols out of books where the editor decides to start verse 7 halfway through verse 2, and you've had to send a search party to attempt to trace verses 4 and 5. If you could somehow simplify it and make it more user-friendly, I would be so grateful."

On receipt of the original copy, I realised it was an even tougher proposition than he had visualised. Verse 1 saw the sopranos happily singing a unison verse on their own, and verse 2 saw straightforward block harmony throughout. The fun began in verse 3 where Choir 1 altos appeared to have the tune, with the full Choir 2 singing the words in harmony, while the sopranos, tenors and basses of Choir 1 took it in turns to "Ah," "Oooh" and "Aw." Turning over five pages brought me to verse 4 where this time the basses of both choirs had the tune, with the tenors of both choirs humming and the sopranos and altos of Choir 1 both appearing to have a well-earned verse off. And so on. By the time I discovered the climactic verse 11, mixed up in the middle of verses 6 and 7 and underneath a picture of a smug looking choirboy who appeared to have sprouted wings up his backside, the first basses were back with the tune, the second tenors were singing a different tune altogether, the altos had gone to put the kettle on, the third sopranos were queuing for turkey stuffing, and everyone else was queuing up for a well-earned pint at the Fleece and Firkin.

By the time I'd finished, four sweaty and irritable hours later, there was no time for any serious Christmas shopping at all. But on the other hand, it was particularly pleasing to present Tripplehorn with 15 copies of the finished article at the start of the practice, and see the look of pleasure and gratitude on his face.

Was therefore a little put out when ninety minutes later, at the end of the practice, we hadn't even looked at *Greet The Gladsome Morn*. When I challenged Tripplehorn, he casually replied "Oh, it's not for us. It's for my friend Clive who runs the East Cambuslang Harmony Revellers. He's thinking of performing it next year or the year after. He only wants one copy. You might as well have these others back. I don't need them."

Made a mental note to reserve Plainsong Adoration for Craig. Tripplehorn will have to be content with the bottom card of my Woolworths 60 for £2 pack. Namely Robin On Sprig Of Holly. In Illfitting Envelope.

Friday 13th December

Queenie's funeral. A huge congregation which, I was told, included a number of former choir members. The service included four of Queenie's favourite hymns, one of her favourite pieces of choral music, namely *Sanctus* from Faure's *Requiem*, some prayers, and some tributes from those closest to her. Apparently she was a great lover of stage musicals, and as well as achieving the accolade of Most Choir Outings Ever Undertaken By A Female Choir Member – no prizes for guessing who came up with that invaluable piece of information – she still found time to pursue a fanatical interest in the stage career of Barbara Streisand, and even auditioned for a regional heat of *Stars In Their Eyes*, as Miss Streisand. Her sister reckoned that had she been ten years younger and her nose two inches longer, she'd have got on the show. "I did hope that your choir could have sung her audition piece, *Don't Rain On My Parade*, this afternoon, but the copy I sent your choirmaster was lost in transit," she said.

It was a lovely service and was followed by a reception in the church hall to which all the choir members were invited. As we got in, I said to Tripplehorn somewhat mischievously "I bet you were gutted that that music went missing." "Devastated," he replied. "Especially as I received it on Wednesday. But, you know, some of my mail does have a very marked tendency to fall straight into my dustbin the moment I get it. And always on the day the refuse collectors come. Care for a cheese and pickle sandwich?"

Having partaken of a cup of tea and a slice of lemon drizzle cake, and exchanged pleasantries with other choir members and one or two of our regular congregation, I didn't think there seemed a lot more to stay for. As I was about to leave, I noticed an attractive girl standing alone looking rather mopey. Feeling almost guilty myself about Tripplehorn's summary disposal of Queenie's favourite song, and wishing to redress the balance slightly, as it were, I went over to her.

"Very sad occasion," I said. "Yes," she replied, with a rather lugubrious smile. "Then again," I said, "I think of this as a celebration of a life well-lived rather than mourning for a life that's been lost." I went on to say how much Queenie had contributed to our corporate lives, how much she meant to us, how stoically she bore many of the trials of life in a choir with its difficult personalities, how she amused us with her stories of past choir exploits, and how she would be sadly missed in the ranks of the second

sopranos. "It's wonderful," I said, bringing in a spiritual element that I felt to be wholly in keeping with the mood of the occasion, "to think that just a few weeks ago she was serving God amongst us, and now she is serving him in his presence." I placed my empty cup down on the nearby table. "By the way," I said, "How do you know Queenie?"
"I don't," she replied. "I'm the caterer."

Sunday 15th December – *THIRD SUNDAY IN ADVENT*
A lovely sunny morning, and a nice service at which we did an excellent *Dixit Maria* although of course we had had an extra week to rehearse it. The Sparkes family were kept very busy with Zoe lighting the three Advent candles, Alison reading the epistle and Matthew singing a small solo section of the plainchant sequence. I had to leave fairly promptly after the service as I was cooking lunch for Brian and Rachel, but there was just time for Cora to collar me as I was leaving, asking if I'd contribute to the entertainment at Friday's party. Anxious to get away, I nodded, then hurried home.
This afternoon was the rehearsal for Wednesday's carol-singing that Ken has organised. It was more of a tea-party than a practice. We got through the music quite quickly – Margaret, Lesley and Ken are all excellent readers, and Brian makes up in volume and enthusiam what he lacks in sightreading skills – then relaxed over tea, mini sausage rolls and home-made shortbread and mince pies. Ken made us laugh when he told us about the Load Of Old Cobblers, a sort of choir subgroup set up by ex-choir member Miranda Cobbledick for the purpose of attempting to sing madrigals and close harmony for local functions – "attempting" being the operative word. "It's rumoured they come out of the woodwork every now and then," he said. "They only need to open their mouths and everyone wishes they'd stayed there."
It was a wonderful afternoon which turned into evening, the tea being replaced by most acceptable red wine, of which we all – Margaret included – had a little too much. I told Ken I'd rashly agreed to perform at the party on Saturday. He thought that was hilarious and said "Well, if you find yourself *Walking In A Winter Wonderland* with Lady 'Engelbert' Willoughby-Smith, don't say I didn't warn you."
Tottered home, very definitely the worse for wear, and listened to my answerphone messages. Ken was wrong of course. It's not *Winter Wonderland* with Cora. It's *Santa Claus Is Coming To Town*. With the Load Of Old Cobblers.

Tuesday 17th December

Woke up feeling snuffly and rather hoarse, and almost certainly running a temperature. Was wondering whether to go into work when Tripplehorn rang to check my availability for the official choir carol-singing tonight. My first impulse was to say neither my voice nor I were feeling up to it, when he went on "It is pretty desperate. We've promised about eight or nine housebound parishioners that we'd go and sing for them. If you can't make it I think we'll have to cancel. Such a shame. I know at least two of those we'll be visiting talk of little else but this for weeks beforehand and it's such a simple but effective way of our giving something of ourselves at this special time of year."

I gulped down some Beechams Powders then staggered along to the church amid bucketing rain and a gale-force south-westerly wind. Alison was there with Zoe and her friends Kylie and Lucy, as were Joan Trumpington and Arthur Ramsbottom. No sign of Tripplehorn at all. When I asked where he was, Arthur told me "He's got a bit of a cold and didn't want to give it to anybody else."

Quite why I didn't use that as a pretext for jumping ship at that moment, I really don't know. I would then have been saved the wettest two hours of my life, the rain – notwithstanding the umbrella I had provided – soaking both my clothing and my music, and sending me home feeling very much worse than I had been at the start, thereby ruling me out of Ken's carol-singing tomorrow night. Almost incidental to the sheer ghastliness of the experience was the torch Joan provided which insisted on cutting out every six and a half seconds; the sulk thrown by Zoe when informed that *Wombling Merry Christmas* was not on our carol sheets; the constant requests, from the occupiers of houses who did respond to our increasingly desperate knocking, for *The First Nowell*, the six verses of which I think we sang eight times, all exactly the same; Arthur Ramsbottom's attempts at providing harmony which varied from singing the tune three bars behind everyone else to warbling the descant two octaves lower; the complete variance between the words in my *Carols For Choirs* book and the words on the sheets that the rest of the singers were sharing one between three; the five minute debate required to ascertain the correct starting note for each carol we sang; the five verses of *Good King Wenceslas* (or, as Joan kept on calling it, *Good King WenceLESSlas*) we sang to a house that turned out to be empty; on arrival at Joan's house for the promised glasses of hot punch and mince pies, the prospect of which was the only thing that had kept me going throughout the evening, discovering that Joan's sister, who was supposed to be providing them, had thought we were coming tomorrow and had gone off to bingo; and, most galling of all, Joan's fit of amnesia which meant that of the nine housebound parishioners, we were only able, after half an hour's exploratory rambling, to locate two, one of whom happened to be profoundly deaf, and the other shouting at us through the letter box that she'd already paid her water rates and if we dared to seize her television set she'd call the police.

Perhaps Zoe had the right idea after all and we should plan our seasonal selection for next year accordingly. Though whether I'll have the time and energy to dust down my Great Uncle Bulgaria costume is of course another matter altogether.

Friday 20th December

At a shortened practice tonight, because of the choir Christmas party afterwards, we concentrated on the easier accompanied carols, leaving the harder work for Sunday afternoon. I rallied well after the disappointment of missing Ken's carol singing on Wednesday night, and was pleased with my solo verse of *In The Bleak Midwinter*. However, my voice still wasn't a hundred per cent, and I thus had the perfect excuse to duck out of the party entertainment. It's an ill wind.

It was a lovely party, with the entertainment reaching a surprisingly high standard. The Load Of Old Cobblers didn't seem to miss me at all. As we were enjoying our food, Tripplehorn appeared with the missing *Carols For Choirs* II books for us to add to our folders. It seems that Joan, for reasons best known to herself, had stored them right at the back of the music cupboard, hidden under a bundle of copies of that landmark work in the history of English musical composition, *Gaily Blow Up The Pipes Of Pan* by Charles Bainbridge Crankshaft FRCO.

My copy seemed rather thicker than most. On opening it I realised why: a spectacular accumulation of unopened envelopes, all addressed to Irving Cattermole and all obviously Christmas cards from years past that he'd been handed on the day of a service or concert but hadn't bothered to take home, still less extract from the envelope. Far from looking sheepish as I handed them to him, he seemed to find the whole thing quite amusing, his amusement increasing when he opened the cards and announced that two of the donors were now dead, one was receiving treatment in some form of psychiatric institution, and one, actually dated four years ago, wished "you and Sylvia many more years of blissful married happiness." I asked why that was so funny. "Only that our decree absolute came through two months later," he chortled, helping himself to a Viennese mincemeat slice.

One less Christmas card for me to write next year, anyway.

169

Sunday 22nd December – *FOURTH SUNDAY IN ADVENT*

A predictably poor congregation this morning and singularly pedestrian music. Tripplehorn not in the best of moods for our afternoon practice. After we'd made a spectacular mess of *The Truth From Above*, he informed us that the fact tht the Christingle service was to take place in church at 5.30pm would not stop him continuing the rehearsal until we got it right. "You mean, find somewhere else to rehearse after 5.30pm?" Lesley queried. "I never said that," he replied.

We did struggle with our unaccompanied pieces. Tripplehorn had great delight, after each piece, in playing the chord we'd just finished on, and then immediately play another chord – the one we should presumably have finished on – as much as a tone higher. When this happened for possibly the twelfth time Henry ventured to say to him "Is our tuning really that bad this afternoon?" "Oh, no," he said. "It's been fine throughout. I just enjoy seeing the look on your faces."

Whatever turns him on, I suppose.

By four thirty we had made up some ground and only had one left to do, Gardner's setting of *The Holly And The Ivy*. At one point the choir split into two, at another into three and another into five, but with no indication as to how that was to be done. Tripplehorn swore blind he'd told us how the split was to happen some weeks ago, but nobody could remember. "It's all right," said Joan. "I've got it all down. Sopranos verse 1, basses verse 2, sopranos and tenors on verse 3 with sopranos doing the top line and tenors the bottom line when they divide, altos and basses on verse 4 with altos doing the top line and basses the bottom line when they divide, full choir on verse 5 with sopranos on top, altos and basses on second line and tenors on third line when they divide, and in verse 6 the first sopranos to divide to do the top two lines, the second sopranos and altos the next line, then the tenors and then the basses. There you are. No problem." There was a stunned silence and a whoop of delight from Tripplehorn. "Sorted. Let's do it," he said, "then we can all go home."

Having ensured our copies were marked with the requisite instructions, we gave a passable rendition of the piece and got ready to go, delighted that what could have been a very long afternoon was finishing much earlier than anticipated. As Tripplehorn was announcing arrangements for tomorrow night, Henry interrupted. "Just a minute," he said. "It can't be right that the basses do verse 2 on their own. Surely the tenors should be with them."

I expected Tripplehorn to ignore the interruption, but surprisingly he didn't, replying "I suppose they could if they wanted to."

"I think it needs clarifying," said Henry Peasgood, warming to his theme. "Taking that logic to extremes, anyone could just sing if they wanted and the whole thing would disintegrate into chaos."

"I'm not happy about the altos doing the second line of verse 5," said Margaret.

"They're not," Irving Cattermole cut in. "They're doing the third line."

"I'm sure we said the sopranos do the first half of verse 3 on their own," Hazel Ledworthy announced.

"I don't think so," said Arthur Ramsbottom. "I've quite definitely got down here that the altos and basses do verse 4 together so for consistency the sops and tenors should do verse 3."

"Yes, together for the second part," Hazel persisted, "but not all of it."

"To be honest," said Alison, "I'm never happy about the sopranos splitting for the final verse. Can't the altos do the second line down?"

"They are doing the second line," Tripplehorn replied.

"Second line as in second stave but not as in the second soprano part," said Alison.

"So what you mean," said Henry Peasgood deliberately, "is that the part underneath the top soprano part and notionally written for second soprano but still on the stave devoted to soprano parts might in fact better be suited not to the second soprano but to the part expecting to sing the music printed on the second stave while the second sopranos while adhering to the first stave sing the music assigned to the first sopranos."

It was forty-five minutes later that we came to a mutually agreeable solution. To do it exactly as Joan had announced it in the first place.

But by then I think most of us would have settled for any compromise deal. Even if it meant ditching the whole carol in favour of providing backing for a cover version of *Bohemian Rhapsody* by the Wednesday Over 80's Aerobics For Arthritics Club.

Monday 23rd December

A lovely surprise – or so I thought – just before the carol service, as Jane Markwick came into the vestry and announced she was singing with us tonight. She gave me a big bear hug and told me how much she'd missed me. But not too much, evidently, for seconds later she produced a young man reeking of cigarette smoke whom she introduced to me as her boyfriend Hal. I was then informed that he would be singing tenor with us tonight.

A magical start to the service, Matthew doing a beautiful solo to verse 1 of *Once In Royal* by a single candlelight, and then a build-up of voices and light during the procession: unaccompanied semichorus verse 2, unaccompanied full choir verse 3, full verses 4 and 5, and after the procession, a rousing descant for verse 6. Beautifully choreographed and very effective.

But things then went spectacularly downhill.

Had our newcomer had a good voice, I'm sure his presence would have been most welcome, but his raucous tones made me doubly annoyed that he had gatecrashed the proceedings without attending any rehearsal. There wasn't a single carol for which he had the right music ready at the start; he succeeded in adding his voice to almost every occasion on which the ladies were singing on their own, he got himself completely lost in the Rutter, he managed to drop all his music to the ground during the fourth reading, scattering bits of paper over a wide area, his nicotine-flavoured breath made me feel sick whenever he opened his mouth to sing, and the last poignant chord of *In The Bleak Midwinter* was drowned out by his machine-gun like burst of coughing.

Afterwards, over "mulled pies and mince wine" as the vicar advertised it at least three times during the evening, I saw Hal having a rather clumsy snog with Jane. More to cheer myself up than anything else, I said to Lesley "I can't see that romance lasting much beyond the turkey and plum pudding."

"Actually," said Lesley, "they've just announced their engagement."

Not that that altogether surprised me. Knowing Jane as I do, it wouldn't actually come as a surprise to learn she was flying off tomorrow to start a new life artichoke farming on the slopes of Rum Doodle.

Tuesday 24th December/Wednesday 25th December – *CHRISTMAS EVE/CHRISTMAS DAY*

Lubricated by a good evening session in the Holly Tree with some surprisingly good impromptu carol singing, we enjoyed what was quite a festive atmosphere in the vestry before the midnight service. A warm handshake from Tripplehorn, cards from several choir members including Jane, and a parcel from Brian and Rachel. And Mr Trimble came into the vestry with an envelope for me and a cry of "Merry Christmas!" Opened the envelope happily expecting another written expression of seasonal greeting, only to discover a list of all the PCC meeting dates for the next 2 years and a handwritten note that the next meeting, on 7 January, is likely to be "very lengthy" and, as if that is not enough, will include a presentation by a Mr Arnold Christleton on Tackling Dry Rot In Ecclesiastical Outbuildings.

Seeing Jane engaging in another passionate embrace with the walking ad for Benson and Hedges, from whom she had been inseparable throughout three rounds of drinks, suddenly made me feel really quite anticlimatical. At that moment I honestly felt like packing in the choir as well as the PCC, for all the good I've been able to bring to or take out of either organisation. Margaret saw my glum look and very sweetly tried to cheer me up. "God will see you're all right," she said.

But try as I might, I just couldn't lift my spirits to exult in the coming of the Saviour of mankind, to share in the joy of the angels, the wonderment of the shepherds, and the worship of the Magi. I was only too pleased when after singing a passable mass setting and what Tripplehorn called "bog standard carols for the once-a-year brigade" I was able to sit and relax while the huge crowds in St Basil's came up to receive communion. In barely eight hours I'd be setting off to the Midlands to spend Christmas Day and Boxing Day with my sister and her family and I decided the change of scene, and a chance to collect my thoughts, couldn't come soon enough.

Fairly predictably, I recognised few of the communicants. The many newcomers certainly brought down the average age, and their fashionable winter outfits made a pleasing change from the severe tweeds and sensible shoes of the normal blue-rinse contingent. Among the visitors was a slim tallish girl who sideways on seemed vaguely familiar. As she returned from communion she looked towards me and smiled, and immediately I recognised her as the caterer at Queenie Haverthwaite's funeral. With her flowing light-brown hair, colourful scarf, long leather coat, short skirt and high-heeled boots she looked absolutely stunning. To my amazement and delight, she made a beeline for me after the service and, introducing herself to me as Katie, she said "I really liked what you said to me at the funeral the other week. It's made me think so much about me and my own spiritual life. So I thought I'd come along tonight." In just a few minutes I established that she was a divorcee with no children, living in town and running her own catering company and, yes, she would love to meet me for a pub lunch on Friday. We exchanged a Christmas kiss and parted.

Remembering Margaret's words, I suddenly felt a great surge of thankfulness and joy. With the church now virtually empty, I stood by the beautiful old crib, placed below the clear south window from which the star-laden skies were visible, and reflected on how God, through my choir membership, had blessed me in a way I could not have thought possible as little as two hours ago. I found myself uttering a prayer of thanksgiving, really conscious of a vibrant spiritual presence; a presence of one who dared to appear in the world as a helpless baby to transform lives and bring peace and goodwill into the hearts of all men, that in receiving the gift of life everlasting, they might devote themselves to the love and service of others.

As I prayed, I heard someone approaching me. Someone whom God had touched during the act of worship, perhaps, similarly moved by the beauty and wonder of this holy night? Another visitor, enchanted by the sight of the crib, seeking to revive memories of the joys of the Nativity story as relayed to them in the happy innocence of childhood? Neither. It was Hazel Ledworthy, who shook a bunch of keys at me, favoured me with an icy stare and barked "Some of us have got homes to go to, you know."

For an insane moment, desirous of bringing my new-found joy and happiness to my spiritual brothers and sisters, I contemplated whether to give her a big hug and a kiss and wish her a merry Christmas. But I thought better of it. It is rather a long time since I took my correspondence course in the Mike Tyson Art Of Self Defence.

Sunday 29th December – *FIRST SUNDAY AFTER CHRISTMAS*

Katie was in church this morning for a surprisingly well-attended service for the first Sunday after Christmas. We did a beautiful *Adam Lay Ybounden* and an equally pleasing, wholly cough-free *In The Bleak Midwinter*. It was a lovely end to my year with the choir of St Basil's.

Afterwards I plucked up the courage to tell the vicar that although I am keen to continue in the choir – I feel it is the least I can offer up to the Lord after the way he has blessed me – I cannot face any more PCC meetings. The vicar smiled and said "I didn't think you could. Frank and I have had a chat and agreed that if you don't want to continue, he will step in as choir rep in your place. Just between ourselves, you achieved three times as much as your predecessor ever did. If you are anxious to continue to serve the choir otherwise than with your excellent singing voice, we've a suggestion for you."

It turns out that the choir vestry is going to need to be pulled down, largely because of severe dry rot. To build a new one, even with lottery funding, is going to be very expensive for us, and I am being asked to spend the next year co-ordinating a initiative to raise the balance of the funding for the project. I won't be expected to go to any PCC meetings; the PCC will just want periodic reports as to progress. It does sound huge fun, and with Katie's support and my revitalised commitment to giving back to God, I can't wait to make a start.

After a lovely afternoon with Katie, I rang Tripplehorn who confirmed what the vicar had told me earlier, and that he would attend the PCC in future, starting with the meeting on 7th January. I didn't think he seemed too pleased, somehow. Like an idiot, I went on "Anyway, the vicar seems to think I achieved three times as much as Hazel Ledworthy." To which he retorted "Well, nought times three still equals nought, doesn't it." I'm beginning to think even the robin on sprig of holly was pushing the boat out.

Tuesday 31st December

Having agreed with Katie that we would spend a quiet New Year's Eve in together, I got a phone call this morning from Brian inviting me to see the New Year in with him and Rachel. When I explained what my plans were, Brian replied "Bring Katie along too. As long as she doesn't mind other choir members being there. We've invited them all."

Before I rang Katie back and put the suggestion to her, I couldn't resist thinking about what she might have to prepare herself for if she were rash enough to agree. On arrival, perhaps the gruesome sight of the Alien monster, otherwise known as Matthew Sparkes sporting the rubber mask he'd found in his Christmas stocking, and being severely admonished by his long-suffering mother Alison who'd been forced to break off from explaining to Zoe that Frank Incense wasn't one of the wise men after all. Moving purposefully towards the drinks table, Henry Peasgood talking eruditely to Arthur Ramsbottom's clumsily-held camcorder about the help he gave Sir David Willcocks in harmonising verse 3 of *See Amid The Winter's Snow* for the 1962 edition of *Carols For Choirs* volume 1, "and how I managed to steer him away from a potentially disastrous cadential 6/4 at the end of the second line," while in the next room the sound of strangled top B flats and smashing glass would clearly indicate Cora Willoughby-Smith warming up for her Assorted *Flying Dutchman* Favourites. Over by the food display, Hazel Ledworthy standing menacingly over her clingfilm-wrapped bakewell tarts, ready to pounce clinically and ruthlessly on anyone foolish enough to help themselves thereof until the savouries had been consumed. Standing at the bottom of the stairs, Jane Markwick in a slinky short black dress, waiting to find an unattached hopeful to flirt with before producing, from nowhere, the man to whom she had just pledged eternal love, namely a Martian with four heads and three noses. In the corner of the room, Irving Cattermole well and truly hemmed in by Craig Dumbleton and his exposition of the joys of the interior furnishings of the booking hall at Turnpike Lane tube station, looking desperately for a kind referee to stop the fight; in the conservatory, an already merry Lesley Markwick hooting with hysterical laughter at a tipsy Tripplehorn likening the rendition by Cora, Joan and Hazel of *Silent Night* on Christmas morning to the deathbed gruntings of an asthmatic hyena; nearby, Margaret Pardew imploring Brian to come and sing at the evangelical church's Easter Monday Christian Teddy

Bear's Picnic. And lastly Joan Trumpington, clutching a tupperware box of oven-ready savoury pancakes, believing today to be Shrove Tuesday.

Rang Katie to ask what whether she would prefer to go to the party or stay at home with me. She listened patiently while I elaborated fully on the membership of St Basil's choir. A choir at the hands of which I had over the past twelve months suffered humiliation, frustration, disappointment, perplexity, bewilderment, astonishment, exasperation, heartache, despair and sheer unbridled fury. A choir that had tested my faith in human nature and the power of God to the limit. A choir that even the strictest malingerer-hating psychiatric doctor would have told me to be rid of within weeks of signing on the dotted line. In seconds we agreed on where we would spend the evening.

Now I just need to phone Brian. To find out what time the party starts.

THE END